What others are saying about this book:

"A comprehensive, practical, and clearly written user's manual."

Jan Axelson, *ComputerCraft* Magazine

"A marvelous book. The explanations of theory and practice are clear and concise, and the historical section is very useful, interesting, and informative. The projects are well designed, the instructions clear, and span the simple to the complex. This book is a must for anyone who wants to really DO something with Muscle Wires."

Dick Prather, Founder, HomeBrew Robotics Club

"Finally, an expert in the field and one of its main enthusiasts, Roger G. Gilbertson, has written a book in straightforward, easy to understand terms. Not only does he tell how shape memory wires work, he also explains how to use them, thus bridging the gap between novice and seasoned expert."

Wayne Brown, from the Foreword

"This book reveals dozens of how's and why's that will open your mind to whole new realms of electronic and mechanical devices. Muscle Wires and this book will definitely expand your bag of tricks."

Paul Harris, Illusionist and Special Effects Artist

"Even for an expert in the field, this book contains a lot of interesting and helpful hints. The projects are great – my favorite is the airplane launcher! I'm sure that these projects will help designers understand the function of shape memory actuators, and will trigger other intelligent ideas."

Dr. Dieter Stöckel, Raychem Metals Division

"Your book is a great help in getting started with nitinol. I wish I'd had it 10 months ago... thanks for a quick response and a great product."

Brian Tillotson, Boeing Space Group

"*Muscle Wires Project Book* contains all the history, theory, and practical application of shape memory alloy wires, the 'muscle' wires. Follow Roger Gilbertson, master experimenter, as he glues, tapes, staples, solders, and rubber bands his 15 projects together, then launch your own imagination. This book is a must for all roboticists."

Brad Smallridge, Director of the Robotics Society of America

"Reading Roger Gilbertson's book is like having an enthusiastic guide glide you through a 3-room learning lab. The first room traces the international history of shape memory alloys, the second offers detailed explanations enriched by clear diagrams of how shape memory alloys work, and the third leads the reader step-by-step to the satisfying completion of 15 different projects of increasing complexity. *Muscle Wires* is an ideal introduction to this fascinating material for the serious new investigator as well as a clearly-written how-to guide of quality projects for the sophisticated hobbyist."

Deborah Gilden, Ph.D., Associate Director
Rehabilitation Engineering Center, Smith-Kettlewell Eye Research Institute

"If you're interested in lightweight robot muscles, check this book out immediately!"

Raymond Côté, *Robot Explorer Newsletter*

MUSCLE
WIRES

PROJECT BOOK

MUSCLE WIRES

PROJECT BOOK

Third Edition
Completely Revised

3.02

Written by **Roger G. Gilbertson**

Edited by **Celene de Miranda**

Designed by **Mark Tuchman**

MONDO•TRONICS

Muscle Wires® Project Book
A Hands-on Guide to Amazing Robotic Muscles that Shorten When Electrically Powered

Third Edition, Completely Revised
Roger G. Gilbertson

Mondo-tronics, Inc.
4460 Redwood Hwy #16-307
San Rafael, CA 94903
USA

Phone: 415-491-4600
Fax: 415-962-4039
Email: mondotronics@email.com
Web: www.Mondotronics.com

Limits of Liability and Disclaimer of Warranty
This book is intended for the education and enlightenment of its readers. Though reasonable care has been taken to ensure its accuracy, the authors assume no responsibility for errors, omissions, or the suitability of its contents for any application. Nor do they assume responsibility for damages resulting from use or misuse of information in this book. The reader is solely responsible for determining if the use, manufacture or sale of devices using information in this book infringes on any patents, copyrights or other rights.

Please note Muscle Wires is a registered trademark of Mondo-tronics, Inc. Betalloy, CryoFit, and Tinel are trademarks of Raychem Corporation. BetaFlex is a trademark of BetaPhase, Inc. BioMetal is a trademark of Toki Corporation. Flexinol is a trademark of Dynalloy, Inc. Macintosh is a trademark of Apple Corporation. Wherever you go, there you are.

Library of Congress Card Catalog Number: 93-77383

ISBN: 1-879896-13-3 (paperback, 3rd edition)
1-879896-14-1 (" with 1 meter Sample Kit)
1-879896-16-8 (" with 3 meter Deluxe Kit)

Publisher's Cataloging In Publication Data
Prepared by Sanford Berman, Head Cataloger at Hennepin County Library, Minnesota.

Gilbertson, Roger G.
    Muscle wires project book. Edited by Celene de Miranda. Designed by Mark Tuchman. 3rd ed, completely revised. San Rafael, CA: Mondo-tronics, copyright 1993, 2000.

    "A hands-on guide to amazing robotic muscles that shorten when electrically powered." Illustrated with drawings, diagrams, and photos.
    PARTIAL CONTENTS: Motorless motion! Basic muscle wire circuit and mechanism. Shape memory alloys around the world. —Muscle wire projects. Linear action and battery power circuit. Basic lever. Ratcheted robot and oscillator circuit. Boris—a motorless six legged walking machine.
    PARTIAL APPENDICES: Pattern sheets. –Soldering electronics. –Triangle actuators. -Electronic symbols.

    1. Shape memory alloy wires. 2. Robotics. 3. Electronic circuits. I. Miranda, Celene de, editor. II. Mondo-tronics. III. Title.

621 or 621.3 or 629.892

Contents

Caution!

This book contains some projects that use voltages which can be dangerous or lethal. Use proper electrical safety procedures at all times, and supervise children working with these projects.

Thanks

Abe Askenazi, Arthur Bebak, Jeff Brown, Wayne Brown, Buckminster Fuller Institute, John Busch, Joan Carlson, Fred DaMert & Company, Anita Flynn, Steven J. Epstein, Andrew Harris, Dr. Darel Hodgson, Dr. Dai Homma, Dr. David Johnson, Vicky Kleban, Scott Orlosky, Chuck Overton, Chris Paine, Jack Palevich, Regenos Design Group, Brad Smallridge, Dr. Dieter Stöckel, Naomitsu Tokieda, Tom Twohy and Wylde Party.

Special Thanks

Christopher Paine, Dan Kaylor, Michael & Victoria Paine, Mark Moorman, John Middendorf IV, F. Ward Paine, Graham & Joyce Gilbertson.

Team Mondo-tronics

Jason Cooper, Sandra Davies, Katharyn Fenske, Roger G. Gilbertson, Edgar Gomez, Karin Hannon, Shawny Kaltenbach, Charles Karp and unfortunately, SLRG the Android.

Cover

Boris, our award-winning motorless walking machine, steps out of the future and on to your work bench. With this book you can build Boris and fourteen other amazing Muscle Wire projects. Photo by David Belda. Cover design by Dan Gilbert.

Dedicated to all the hard working creators of the shape memory alloy field, and to the long term supporters of this publication. All of their continuing efforts made this book possible.

Foreword

The first encounter between those who know about shape memory wires and those first learning about them has, until now, been like the fabled meeting between East and West —

while speaking with the same words, the differing backgrounds of the individuals lead each of them to separate conclusions.

The expert may entertain the newcomer with strange and surprising demonstrations of what the wires can do. The novice may be awed by the seeming reversal of natural laws, but leaves feeling like he has just seen a magic show instead of learning useful information about a subject with far-reaching uses.

The breakdown in communication lies in the gap that separates professionals from lay people. Often, professionals seem to have different meanings for their words.

For example, the lay person may ask "how can a wire have a memory?" But when explained with "lattice structures", "crystal states" and "phase changes" the gap widens until the newcomer wonders what this all has to do with an obviously interesting and useful material.

With this book, all that has changed. Finally, an expert in the field and one of its main enthusiasts, Roger G. Gilbertson, has written a book in straightforward, easy to understand terms. Not only does he tell how shape memory wires work, he also explains how to use them, thus bridging the gap between novice and seasoned expert.

The industry has needed a book like this for some time, and it is a book sure to become the introductory textbook for a growing number of interested readers. We wholeheartedly recommend this book as a valuable tool for the practical minded person interested in shape memory alloys.

Wayne Brown
President
Dynalloy, Inc.

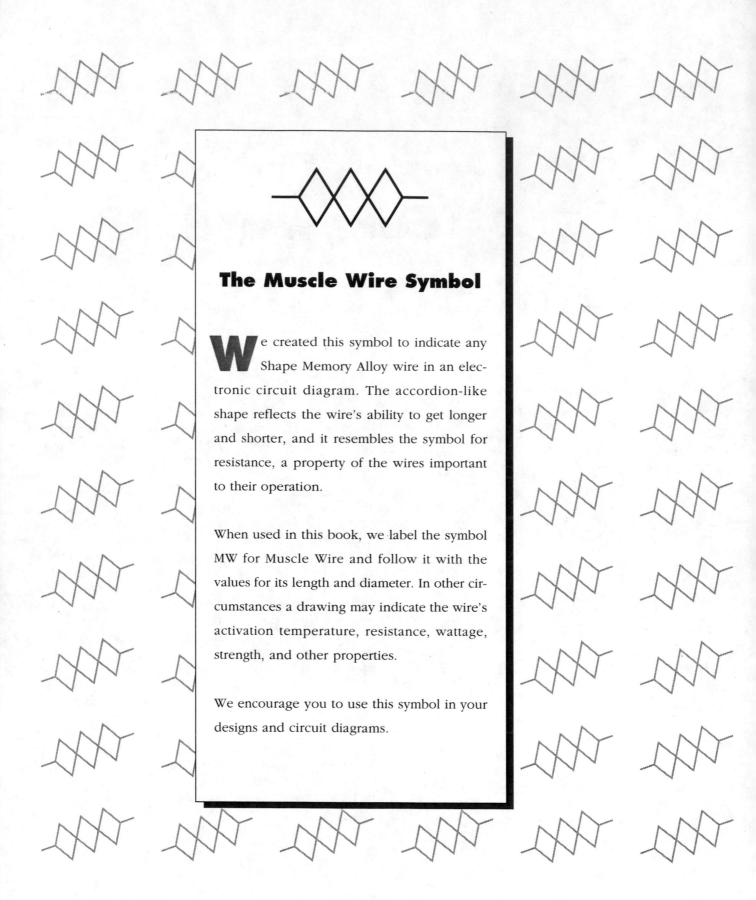

The Muscle Wire Symbol

We created this symbol to indicate any Shape Memory Alloy wire in an electronic circuit diagram. The accordion-like shape reflects the wire's ability to get longer and shorter, and it resembles the symbol for resistance, a property of the wires important to their operation.

When used in this book, we label the symbol MW for Muscle Wire and follow it with the values for its length and diameter. In other circumstances a drawing may indicate the wire's activation temperature, resistance, wattage, strength, and other properties.

We encourage you to use this symbol in your designs and circuit diagrams.

Roger G. Gilbertson

PART ONE

Motorless Motion!

There are two very common ways to create motion from electricity; motors and solenoids. You can find these two inventions almost everywhere. In fact, there are probably some present in the room with you right now.

Motors use coils of conductive wire to generate magnetic fields and create continuous rotation. You'll find motors in refrigerators, washers, dryers, garbage disposers, record, tape and CD players, computer disk drives, answering machines, fans, vacuum cleaners, blenders, can openers, razors, hedge trimmers, lawn mowers, toys, and numerous others.

The second device, the solenoid, uses coils of wire to make a magnetic field and push or pull with a single stroke. Speaker coils are one kind of solenoid, and you will also find them in door bell strikers, old style telephone ringers (newer ringers use crystalline *piezoelectric* materials that create small, strong vibrations when subjected to high voltages), electric door locks, and you'll find solenoids in pinball machines by the dozen.

But there is a very different and much newer way to create motion from electricity — *Shape Memory Alloys* (SMAs). These special metals undergo changes in shape and hardness when heated or cooled, and do so with great force.

Of the many names for these materials (shape memory alloys, memory metals, nitinol, etc.) we've chosen *Muscle Wires* to indicate our specially processed SMAs in wire form that contract in length when heated.

Muscle Wires pull with a surprisingly large force — capable of lifting *thousands* of times their own weight — and move silently with a smooth, life-like quality. They can be heated directly with electricity, and can be used to create a wide range of motions, operating quickly and with precise controlability.

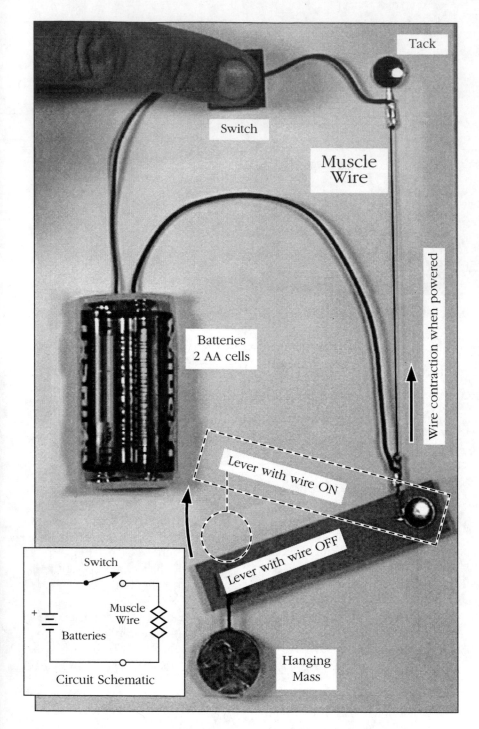

Figure labels: Tack, Switch, Muscle Wire, Wire contraction when powered, Batteries 2 AA cells, Lever with wire ON, Lever with wire OFF, Hanging Mass

Circuit Schematic: Switch, +, Batteries, Muscle Wire

Figure 1.0   A Basic Muscle Wire Device
This basic device demonstrates how a Muscle Wire shortens when electrically powered and lifts a lever and mass against gravity. This device contains all the basic systems required for powering, controlling, driving and transforming the motion of a Muscle Wire. The schematic (inset) shows the electrical connections of the battery, switch and wire. The two AA batteries provide about 3 Volts and 200 milliamps to heat the wire. The ten centimeter long wire shortens by four percent of its length (four millimeters), and the lever arm transforms the wire's small, strong motion into a much larger action. When unpowered, the Muscle Wire cools and relaxes, ready for more contractions.

This book lets you discover the amazing properties and abilities of Muscle Wires and proven ways of connecting, powering and controlling them. With Muscle Wires you can build unique and interesting devices that would be difficult or impossible to make using motors, solenoids, or any other method.

All the circuits and devices in this book can be readily adapted to your projects: toys, games, industrial devices, model railroads, model rocketry, science fair projects, animation for doll houses, fantastic magic illusions, devices for radio controlled cars and planes, motion picture special effects, super miniature motorless robotics — your imagination is the only limit!

Once familiar with the basics of Muscle Wires, you can adapt them to your own projects, and soon you will be building a world of novel and exciting creations.

Welcome to a new realm of motorless electro-mechanical motion!

A Basic Muscle Wire Circuit and Mechanism

The device shown in Fig. 1.0 gives an example of a single Muscle Wire powered by two AA batteries. When powered, the Muscle Wire contracts to lift the lever and the weight against gravity. This device contains each of the parts found in any Muscle Wire system:

Power System — *Provides energy to heat the Muscle Wire and drive any supporting electronics. In this example two AA batteries supply just enough power for the wire.*

Control System — *Provides "on and off" control to operate the Muscle Wire. In this case control is*

provided by the action of the operator's finger, eyes and brain.

Driver System — *A part of the electrical system that limits the power to the Muscle Wire, and protects it from damage due to overheating. In this case, the batteries have their own internal resistance which limits the maximum amount of current they can produce, and the batteries' size is matched to the length and diameter of the Muscle Wire.*

Muscle Wire — *Provides the action, and is powered, controlled and protected by the other systems. It must be well connected both mechanically and electrically to the rest of the device.*

Mechanism — *Includes the crimps, lever, mounting base and all other parts that support the Muscle Wire, and permit it to act in the desired manner. The mechanism also protects the Muscle Wire from overstretching, sharp bends and other forces which could damage or degrade its performance.*

For more detail on building this device see Project 2, Basic Lever, starting on page 3-6.

How Muscle Wires Work

Muscle Wires belong to a class of metal alloys displaying a property called the *Shape Memory Effect* (SME). These *Shape Memory Alloys* (SMAs) have a uniform crystal structure that radically changes to a different structure at a distinct temperature.

When the memory alloy is below this "transition temperature" it can be stretched and deformed without permanent damage, more so than most metals. After the alloy has been stretched, if it is heated (either electrically or by an exter-

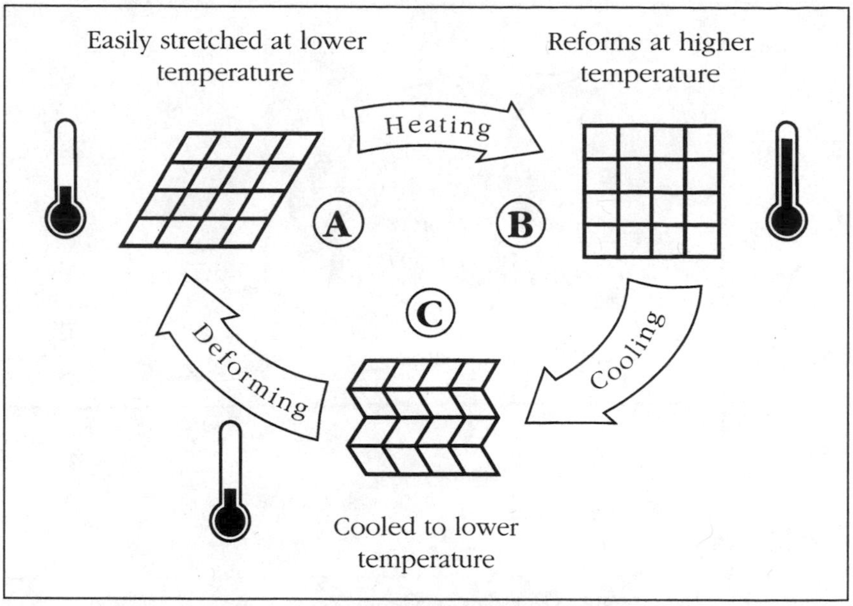

Figure 1.1   Mechanics of the Shape Memory Effect
The grids represent the crystal structure in a typical Shape Memory Alloy (SMA), with each square having a uniform mix of the alloy's component metals. The metal deforms easily when below its transition temperature (A) and the crystal's boundaries shift but do not suffer permanent damage. Heating the alloy to above its transition temperature causes the crystals to undergo a *phase change* and return to their original shape (B); they do so with a large force — several times greater than the force needed to deform them. When again cooled below the transition temperature, the phase change reverses (C) and the metal can be easily deformed once more.

nal heat source) above its transition temperature, the alloy "recovers" or returns to the unstretched shape and completely undoes the previous deforming.

When made into wires, shape memory alloys can be stretched by as much as eight percent when below the transition temperature, and when heated, they will recover their original, shorter length, and contract with a usable amount of force in the process. Figure 1.1 shows this deform/reform cycle.

Shape Memory Alloys have been made using many different combinations of metal elements. The transition temperature varies for each alloy, and can be set during manufacturing by carefully controlling

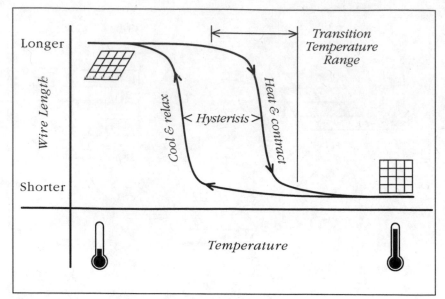

Figure 1.2   Temperature vs. Muscle Wire Length
This graph shows how a Muscle Wire under a constant force changes length as the temperature changes. A typical Muscle Wire relaxes at a lower temperature than it contracts. This difference forms a *hysteresis*, or a range where the wire can be either contracted or relaxed, depending on its starting state.

the ratios of the component metals, and the presence of other elements.

The most common memory alloy, *nitinol* (pronounced "night in all"), consists of nearly equal amounts of nickel and titanium atoms. Differences of less than one percent in their ratio can change the alloy's transition temperature in the range of -100°C to over 100°C.[1]

Alloys intended for use at room temperature (around 20°C) have transition temperatures near 70°C. Alloys with relatively high transition temperatures can be cycled faster since they cool more quickly at room temperature, but require more heating (and thus more power) to activate. Alloys that have transition temperatures below room temperature generally need to be cooled to their relaxed state, but will remain active when kept at room temperature.

In actual operation SMAs exhibit a temperature *hysteresis*, or gap between the contraction and relaxation temperatures, whereby the activation occurs at a slightly higher temperature than the relaxation. (For another example of hysteresis note how, in a conventional light switch, the light turns "on" at one point, but "off" at a slightly different position when flipped the other way.) Figure 1.2 shows a typical temperature-versus-contraction curve for Muscle Wires and the hysteresis in their operation.

A Brief History of Muscle Wires

In 1932, Swedish researcher Arne Ölander observed the shape recovery abilities of a gold-cadmium alloy (Au-Cd), and noted its potential for creating motion.[2] In 1950, L.C. Chang and T.A. Read, at Columbia University in New York, used X-rays to study this unusual alloy and to understand the changes in its crystal structure.[3] They showed that mechanical systems could use the shape memory effect to perform physical work.

The Chang and Read studies sparked further investigations and led to the eventual discovery of an indium-titanium SMA.[4] However, both these alloys proved problematic, as the expense of gold and indium, and the toxic nature of cadmium limited additional research efforts. Then, in 1963, the announcement of a less expensive and non-toxic shape memory alloy initiated a new wave of discovery.

While searching for non-corrosive marine alloys, a team led by W.J. Buehler at the U.S. Naval Ordnance Laboratory (NOL) observed the shape memory effect in an alloy of nickel and titanium. They named the alloy nitinol, an acronym of NIckel, TItanium and NOL.[5] This Ni-Ti alloy generated new interest in

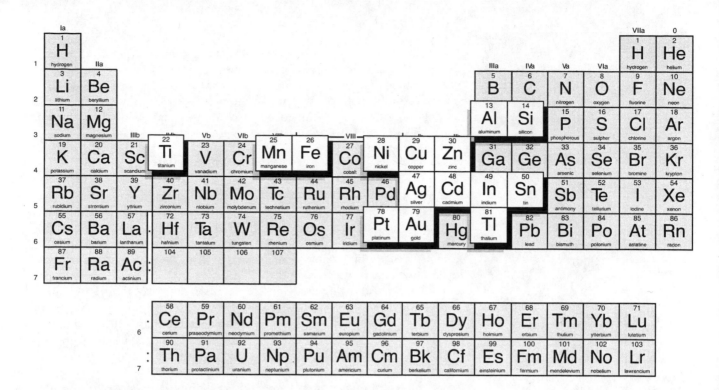

Figure 1.3   The Periodic Table of the Elements
The highlighted elements have been found to display the Shape Memory Effect (SME) in certain combinations including gold-cadmium (Au-Cd), silver-cadmium (Ag-Cd), copper-aluminum-nickel (Cu-Al-Ni), copper-tin (Cu-Sn), copper-zinc (Cu-Zn), copper-zinc-aluminum (Cu-Zn-Al), indium-titanium (In-Ti), indium-thalium (In-Tl), iron-platinum (Fe-Pt), nickel-aluminum (Ni-Al), iron-manganese-silicon (Fe-Mn-Si), manganese-copper (Mn-Cu), and the most common: nickel-titanium (Ni-Ti).

the SMA field, because it was safer, less expensive, and had a better deformation-to-recovery ratio than earlier alloys.

More studies followed, and between 1969 and 1973 researchers found the shape memory effect in other alloys, including copper-aluminum-nickel, copper-tin, copper-zinc, copper-gold-zinc, copper-zinc-aluminum, iron-platinum, nickel-aluminum, and manganese-copper.[6]

On the periodic table of the elements these metals generally rest in close proximity to each other. When alloyed in the combinations detailed in Figure 1.3 they have identical crystal structures displaying the shape memory effect.[7] Nickel-titanium and copper-zinc-aluminum

evolved as the alloys of choice mainly for their strength, low cost and large shape changing abilities.

Applications

During the 1960's and 1970's researchers worldwide worked to develop uses for these metals. NASA studied memory alloys for satellite antennas that would unfold and expand when exposed to the heat of the sun.[8] University, corporate and private researchers explored many uses, including a variety of engines that ran only on hot and cold water, automatic temperature-controlling greenhouse windows, hot water pipe valves, and automobile fan clutches that engaged when the engine reached a specific temperature.

Figure 1.4   The TiNi-1 Engine
TiNi Alloy Company's *TiNi-1 Engine* uses a single coil of nitinol wire and can develop speeds of 1000 RPM on just hot and cold water.

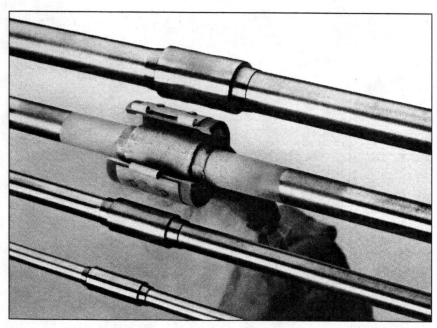

Figure 1.5   CryoFit Couplings
Installed at low temperatures, these pipe fittings shrink into place and provide highly reliable connections for aircraft hydraulic lines. They are one of the most successful shape memory alloy products to date. Photo: Raychem Corporation.

Many early ideas did not pass beyond the research stage. Some were limited by the slow speeds and variable quality of the available alloys, others were limited by their design, and the inventor's lack of experience with SMAs.

But, as the alloys and manufacturing techniques improved, so did the experience and results of the experimenters. Nitinol received much attention for medical applications because, like stainless steel, nickel-titanium alloys have a high compatibility with living tissue and low chance of rejection when implanted.[9]

In 1971, P.N. Sawyer and M. Page of Brooklyn, New York, made an experimental artificial heart using electrically activated 500 micrometer (μm) nitinol wires.[10] However, it ran at 12 to 15 beats per minute, far slower than the normal human 70 to 90 b.p.m. Other experimenters developed braces and tooth alignment structures for dentistry (currently a very common use for SMAs) and blood clot filters that could be easily inserted into veins or arteries, and would then expand into place as they warmed.[11]

Heat Engines

Because shape memory alloys can perform useful work with relatively small temperature differences, researchers looked for ways to use heat from the sun, thermal sources like geysers, and "waste heat" from industrial processes to produce energy. R. Banks at Lawrence Berkeley Laboratory received much attention for the offset crank engine he developed.[12]

This engine used solar heated water to activate SMA wires and turn a shaft. The engine reportedly ran for millions of cycles, and at 60 to 80 revolutions per minute, could generate more than half a watt of power (about enough to light a small Christmas light bulb).

In 1974, A.D. Johnson, also at Lawrence Berkeley Laboratory, and J.S. Cory, a private researcher in Southern California, independently devised a faster SMA thermal engine with the potential for large-scale applications. Based on the Chinese differential pulley (invented around 1000 A.D.), a commercially available model of this engine, called the TiNi-1 Engine (Fig. 1.4) vividly illustrates its ability using just hot and cold water. It can develop speeds of 1000 RPM, and power up to 1 watt.[13] Johnson and Cory eventually met and collaborated on additional SMA research.

In 1980, McDonnell Douglas Company demonstrated a scaled-up nitinol heat engine using nearly one hundred 50 μm diameter nitinol wires. The wires, mechanically connected to each other, passed through baths of cold and hot water. The engine produced power in excess of 32 watts (about 1/15 horsepower) — the largest output for a nitinol heat engine demonstrated to that date.

This engine demonstrated the feasibility of scaled-up designs for nitinol powered thermal engines, and the study concluded "no fundamental problems were found which would prevent development of large and economically competitive Nitinol heat engines." [14]

Other Shape Memory Alloy Products

The late 1970's saw the development of several commercially successful SMA products. Raychem Corporation, based in Menlo Park, California, began researching SMAs in 1967. In the early 1970's they introduced products using two alloys: Betalloy, a copper-zinc SMA, and Tinel, a nickel-titanium alloy with a sub-zero transition temperature.

Most of Raychem's SMA products operated by external temperature sources. Their CryoFit couplings, high performance Tinel cylinders for joining aircraft hydraulic lines (now made by Advanced Metal Components, Inc.), are shipped and installed at liquid nitrogen temperatures (minus 200°C). As they warm, they fittings shrink in diameter by about eight percent, and provide a tight, flawless seal. In 1989 Raychem reported that of over one million parts in service, not one had leaked or failed.[15]

In 1984 a group from Raychem Corporation founded BetaPhase Inc., in Menlo Park, California. They produce a line of electrical con-

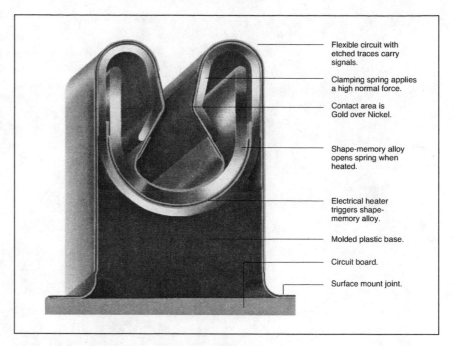

Figure 1.6   BetaFlex Circuit Board Connector
These connectors provide high density connections for computer printed circuit boards. When electrically heated, the SMA actuator opens a spring clamp and permits easy insertion and removal of the circuit board. Courtesy Beta Phase, Inc.

nectors (Fig. 1.6) for high density circuit boards. When heated by a separate internal heating element, a memory alloy actuator presses open a spring and permits insertion or removal of a circuit board. The connector's design accommodates over 190 signal lines per centimeter.[16]

Dr. F.E. Wang, one of the discoverers of nitinol at the Naval Ordnance Labs, founded Innovative Technology International in Beltsville, Maryland. ITI produces several unique SMA powered toys, including a boat that runs on ice cubes and a very simple thermal engine that uses just a single memory alloy loop.[17]

Shape Memory Alloys Around the World

Numerous other individuals and corporations, both large and small, in the United States, Europe and Asia contributed to the advance of

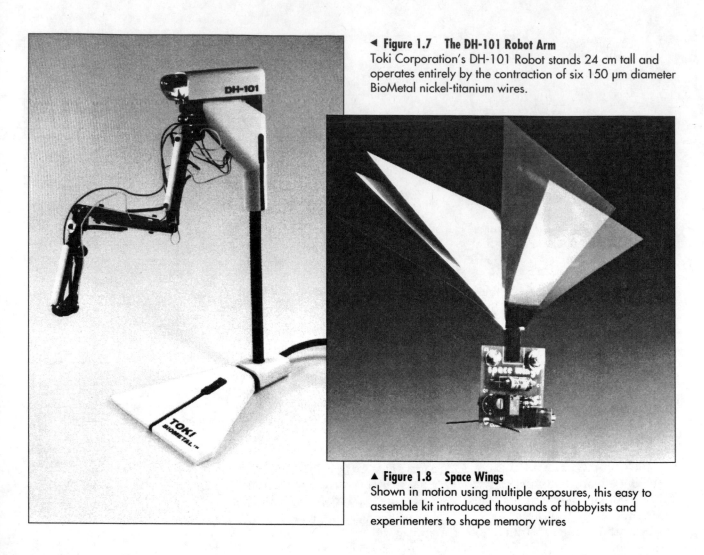

◄ **Figure 1.7   The DH-101 Robot Arm**
Toki Corporation's DH-101 Robot stands 24 cm tall and operates entirely by the contraction of six 150 μm diameter BioMetal nickel-titanium wires.

▲ **Figure 1.8   Space Wings**
Shown in motion using multiple exposures, this easy to assemble kit introduced thousands of hobbyists and experimenters to shape memory wires

SMAs.[18] In England, Germany and Japan, the study of nitinol's properties and crystal structures started in the mid 1960's, mainly at colleges and universities.

Students and professors characterized basic alloy properties and developed demonstration devices. Frequently, graduate students and other researchers joined the staffs of corporations to continue their work. Eventually, some of their developments became products.

In England, Delta Metals was an early investigator and product developer, exploring many thermally activated applications such as automatic greenhouse vents, hot water valves and fan clutches. In Japan, Sharp Electric Company and Matsushita Electric used SMAs to control dampers in electric ovens and to move vent louvers on air conditioners. National (called Panasonic in the U.S.) manufactured a coffee maker that used a Ni-Ti spring as both a temperature sensor and an actuator.[19]

In the early 1980's, Dai Homma, a student at Tokyo's Waseda University, developed an improved method for processing Ni-Ti wires for electrical activation that permitted devices to operate much longer without wire failure. Homma and others, notably Hitachi Corporation and Furukawa Electric, demonstrated medium and small sized robotic arms and hands that oper-

ated entirely by electrically heated SMA wires (Fig. 1.13). Naomitsu Tokieda, the president of Toki Corporation in Tokyo, Japan, expressed interest in developing Homma's discoveries into a commercial product. Upon graduation, Dr. Homma joined Toki which, in 1985, began making an improved, long-lived nitinol wire with the trade name BioMetal. Toki focused on producing and marketing a standard, electrically activated SMA wire for a wide range of applications — a first in the field.

Toki produced high quality wires having a very low deformation force (requiring only a small external force to elongate them when cool), and with very uniform diam-

Figure 1.9   Kinetic Butterfly
Space Wing's more life-like cousin brought motorless animation to store window displays around the world.

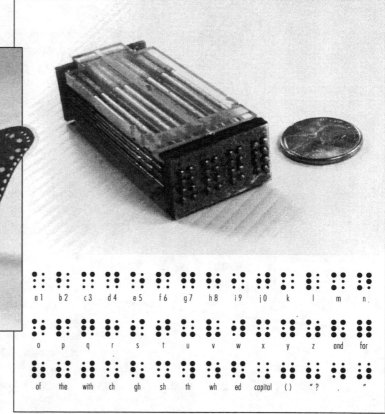

Figure 1.10   Braille Character Display
This award winning Braille display device uses computer controlled shape memory wires to activate eight movable bumps that generate the characters that make up the Braille alphabet for the blind.

eters to minimize hot spots when heated. Most importantly, these wires would regularly perform for millions of cycles when used in properly designed mechanisms.

Toki demonstrated many devices using BioMetal wire including air valves, latches, display actuators, AC lamp oscillators, fuse protectors, high speed oscillators (60 cycles per second and higher) and even a computer-controlled six-action robotic arm (Fig. 1.7).

The high quality and standardized performance of Toki's processed SMA wires provided the springboard for additional developments. In 1985, Wayne Brown, a business consultant and pioneer in micro-

computer-based office automation, started TokiAmerica Technologies and began widely promoting Toki Corporation's BioMetal technology in the United States and Europe.

In 1986, after learning about BioMetal and working with Brown and Tokieda, Roger Gilbertson, Dan Kaylor and Christopher Paine founded Mondo-tronics, Inc. in Sunnyvale, California. They began producing and distributing SMA products and educational kits to experimenters, students, hobbyists and researchers. One kit, a small winged circuit board called Space Wings (Fig. 1.8), developed into Kinetic Butterflies, a line of life-like moving butterflies for store window displays (Fig. 1.9).[20]

At the same time Dr. David Johnson and Scott Orlosky at the TiNi Alloy Company in Oakland, California, developed a more complex device that used BioMetal wires to move eight pins in a Braille character display (Fig. 1.10).

Their award winning design permitted a computer to show Braille text for blind persons to read by touch.[21] The small size of the units allowed them to be easily combined into larger panels. A three line, 60 character display used 480 individual BioMetal wires, and received signals from a standard portable computer.

In 1989, Dr. Darel Hodgson, a metallurgist and memory alloy consul-

BENEFITS OF MUSCLE WIRES

- Low cost
- Small size
- Light weight
- Low power
- Strong force
- Precise control
- High strength-to-weight ratio
- Electric or thermal activation
- Direct linear action
- Versatile arrangements
- Silent operation
- Long lifetime

tant with years of experience at Raychem and BetaPhase, joined with Wayne Brown of TokiAmerica to produce and distribute an improved line of high quality, pre-trained shape memory alloy wires named Flexinol.

Their new company, Dynalloy Inc., combined Hodgson's experience in SMA manufacturing with Brown's knowledge of marketing and SMA applications. Dynalloy emphasizes aiding developers of commercial and industrial SMA applications. Their Flexinol product line features wires having a wide range of strengths, low cost and broad application possibilities. The projects in this book use Flexinol Muscle Wires, and serve as excellent examples of the capabilities, ease of use, and cost effectiveness of SMA wires.

Continuing Explorations

SMA research continues around the world. In 1986, China hosted the International Symposium on Shape Memory Alloys which saw the presentation of seventy-eight papers from fourteen countries. Topics included basic alloy studies, crystal structures, medical applications, product designs, and manufacturing research.[22]

In 1988, Raychem Corp. and Memory Metals Inc., of Norwalk, Connecticut sponsored a conference "Engineering Aspects of Shape Memory Alloys" at Michigan State University.[23] Presentations included thermal and electrical actuators, spring design, automotive and safety equipment, disk drive head lifters, circuit breakers, and a range of medical and surgical applications.

With the dissolution of the Soviet Union, much has been learned about SMA research in Russia. During the 1970's and 1980's the Soviet Union developed their ability to produce nitinol in quantity, and although SMAs were a scarce item for most researchers there, the military produced and stockpiled tons of raw and processed nitinol.[24]

With the many changes and moves towards a free market economy, scientific and research institutions in Russia are now looking to apply their SMA knowledge and experience to various commercial products. Proposals include SMA bone fracture clamps, devices to prevent some types of miscarriage during pregnancy, and even contraceptive devices using nitinol.[25]

Given the availability of inexpensive production facilities, skilled researchers, and a large stockpile

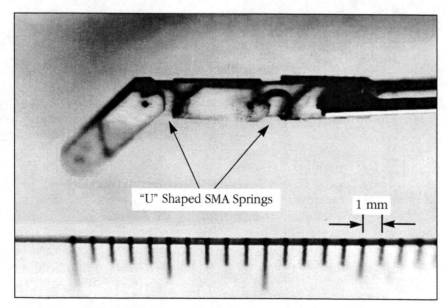

"U" Shaped SMA Springs

1 mm

Figure 1.11   Mini-mechanical Finger Actuator
This small prototype finger, shown five times actual size, was fabricated from a thin ceramic sheet, and moves using tiny "U" shaped Shape Memory Alloy springs.[26] Photo courtesy of Katsutoshi Kuribayashi, Department of Mechanical Engineering, University of Osaka Prefecture, Japan.

of basic materials, Russia could become a major supplier of SMA materials and services in the coming years, if their current quest for marketable products continues.

In 1989, Oaktree Automation, Inc., in Alexandria, Virginia, started developing the Fingerspelling Hand (Fig. 1.12), an anthropomorphic robotic device to serve as a tactile communication aid for deaf-blind individuals, particularly those unable to read Braille. The hand acts as a computer display, presenting one character at a time using a finger spelling alphabet. The user places their hands lightly on the device and "reads" each letter or character by feeling them, one at a time. Data can come from a keyboard, modem, page scanner or closed caption TV decoder.

The Fingerspelling Hand used a total of one hundred and eight 250 µm Flexinol wires acting in parallel. Opposing wires provided flexion and extension for each joint, as well as adduction and abduction (side to side) motions.

Oaktree Automation collaborated with Gallaudet University on the Fingerspelling Hand, with funding from the U.S. Department of Education. Oaktree continues to develop the hand with the goal of commercial production, and founder Phillip Shaw envisions advanced "full arm" SMA driven manipulators for automation, telerobotic operations and assisting mobility impaired people.[27]

To scale down the size of shape memory actuators, TiNi Alloy Company adapted the techniques used to make computer chips and developed ways to form nitinol shapes on silicon. These thin Ni-Ti films can be used for creating very small mechanisms. Even on the

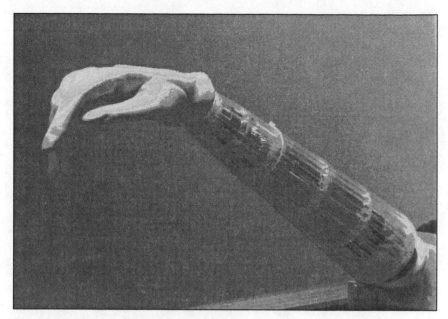

Figure 1.12   Fingerspelling Hand
The anthropomorphic (human-like) Fingerspelling Hand presents data from a computer one character at a time using a finger spelling alphabet. The forearm houses over one hundred individual 250 µm diameter Flexinol Muscle Wires, and thin cords acting like tendons extend the wire's actions to the fingers and wrist. Photo courtesy Oaktree Automation, Inc.

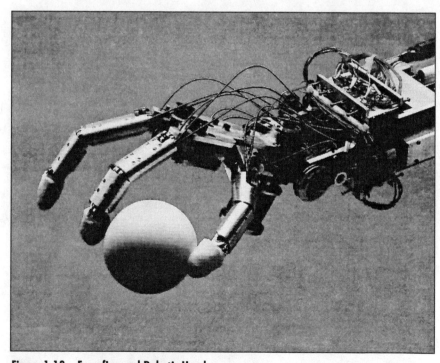

Figure 1.13   Four-fingered Robotic Hand
Hitachi, Ltd. developed this experimental hand in the mid-1980's. The forearm housed twelve groups of 200 µm diameter nitinol wires (four per finger) that closed the hand when powered. When unpowered, springs opened the hand and extended the wires.[28] Photo courtesy Robotics Age.

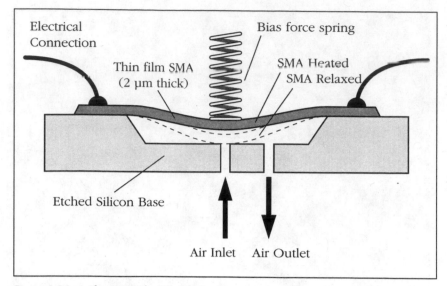

Figure 1.14   Thin SMA Film Micro Valve
Formed out of silicon with a 2 μm thick layer of nitinol, this super miniature valve opens and closes in less than 15 milliseconds. When powered, the thin nickel-titanium layer shortens and rises, permitting the air to flow. When turned off, a bias spring deforms the Ni-Ti layer, closing the inlet and stopping the air flow.

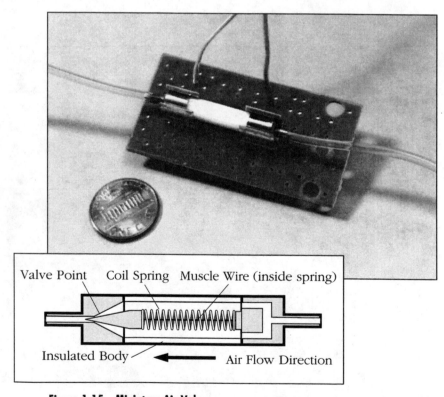

Figure 1.15   Miniature Air Valve
The size of a standard fuse, this air valve needs less than one volt to activate the short Muscle Wire inside, and can regulate pressure up to 0.4 MPa (60 psi). It can also act as a variable analog valve, a difficult task for conventional solenoid-operated valves. Designed by Dr. Dai Homma.

microscopic scale, nitinol has an extremely high strength for its size – much larger than the electrostatic (static electricity) or piezoelectric forces often employed in micromechanical devices.

In 1990 TiNi Alloy demonstrated a thin film SMA valve using a chemically etched silicon base layer and a Ni-Ti coating only 2 to 3 μm thick (Fig. 1.14). When powered, this valve opened in less than 15 milliseconds. When switched off the film cooled and the valve closed equally fast. With ports 200 μm in diameter, the valve had a flow rate of 1 liter per minute at a pressure of 0.14 MPa (20 psi). Because the thin film deforms by only two percent, such valves could operate reliably for millions of cycles.[29]

Hot Developments

More hot topics in SMA research include mechanical switching units for optical communication fibers,[30] electrically activated non-explosive bolts released by an SMA element for sea and space applications,[31] compact fingertip stimulators (Fig. 1.17) or "tactors" for "virtual reality" input/output devices,[32] and thin films of nitinol for creating mini- and micro-mechanical devices[33] having potential for very small robotic systems (Fig 1.11).

Shape memory alloys can now be found in a wide range of applications and products that take advantage of their thermal recovery and superelastic properties. These include orthodontic arch wires[34] where preformed structures can be greatly deformed for easier installation, flexible catheters, and surgical guidewires[35] which are implanted and anchored before an operation as guides to a tumor or other site, and expandable blood

Figure 1.16 Simon Nitinol Filter
Developed by Dr. Morris Simon over a 15 year span, this tiny web of nitinol is inserted into a patient's vein or artery to trap potentially stroke-causing blood clots. During insertion the filter remains in the long form (A) and is kept cool by chilled saline solution. When in place, it warms and opens by the heat of the body (E). The filter can be installed in less than 30 minutes and requires only a small puncture opening. Photo courtesy Nitinol Medical Technologies, Inc.

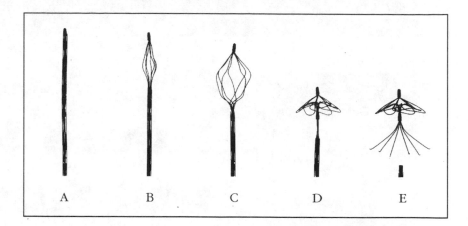

A   B   C   D   E

clot filters[11] (Fig. 1.16) installed inside a vein or artery in a collapsed form and expanded by the warmth of the body.

Other consumer uses include SMA under-wire brassieres[19] for flexible support that recover their original shape with just the heat of a dryer, and superelastic SMA eyeglass frames[36] that withstand bending much like plastic ones (Fig. 1.18).

New manufacturing methods for SMAs include "spin melt" techniques that form molten metal directly into thin wires.[37] Increased sales volumes, new and improved alloys, and greater awareness of the abilities of SMAs all promise to greatly expand the number and diversity of applications. This will further reduce their cost and increase their attractiveness for use in more products.

And as researchers and product developers keep pace with these advances, we will continue to see exciting new uses and applications for shape memory alloys and Muscle Wires. Faster, cheaper and stronger — this fast growing field just *keeps on moving.*

Figure 1.17 "Tactor" A Tactile Feedback Device for Fingertip Stimulation
A short Muscle Wire (inside small rectangle at end of cord) presses a bump against the fingertip to provide touch feedback from computers, in "virtual reality" environments, and teleoperated systems (see Fig. 1.25 and 1.26). Developed by TiNi Alloy Company, these devices are small enough to be mounted on keyboards, gloves and even on tool handles to provide unobtrusive "eyes free" electronic feedback.

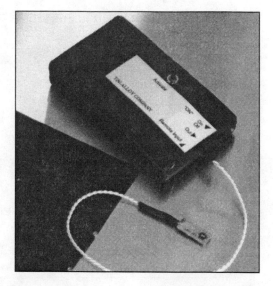

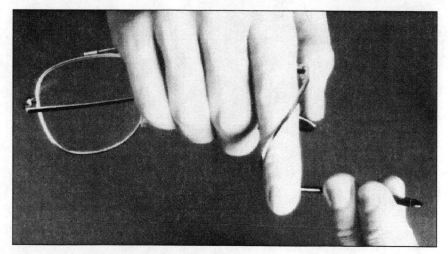

Figure 1.18 Super-elastic SMA Eyeglass Frames
These eyeglass frames use the super-elastic properties of a nickel-titanium alloy in its high temperature austenite phase to provide durable, lightweight and corrosion resistant eye wear. Photo courtesy Marchon Eyewear, Inc.

Future Ideas and Future Applications

A single Muscle Wire can exert an extremely high force for its small mass. Improved alloy formulation, new processing methods and most importantly, new mechanisms and circuit designs stand to greatly increase the overall efficiency and usefulness of devices operated by groups of Muscle Wires.

Wire Size	Quantity[†]	Total Force	Total Lift	Total Power[††]
50 µm	10	3.43 N	0.35 kg	1. Watt
"	50	17.2	1.75	6
"	100	34.3	3.50	13
"	250	85.8	8.75	32
100 µm	10	14.7	1.5	5
"	50	73.5	7.5	24
"	100	147.0	15.0	49
"	250	367.5	37.5	122
150 µm	10	32.3	3.3	8
"	50	161.7	16.5	40
"	100	323.4	33.0	80
"	250	808.5	82.5	200
250 µm	10	91.1	9.3	20
"	50	455.7	46.5	100
"	100	911.4	93.0	200
"	250	2278.5	232.5	500

[†] Wire length: 10 cm   [††] Power used in typical contraction 0.5 sec long.

Figure 1.19   Strengths of Multiple Muscle Wires Lifting In Parallel
For greater strength devices can use many Muscle Wires in parallel. This table shows the forces generated by groups of wires of various sizes, how much weight they can lift, and the total power needed to activate them. Multiple Muscle Wire actuators will make possible many new and useful devices.

Future advances will permit Muscle Wires to spread into many new and exciting applications. One main area for future development involves using multiple wires to create larger and stronger devices.

When acting together, groups of Muscle Wires can exert very large forces. Figure 1.19 shows some examples of groups of wires and their collective strength. Compact, light and very strong actuators can be built by combining many wires into a single device.

On the following pages we present just a few of the directions in which Muscle Wire devices could advance. We invite you to continue these explorations, and to expand their uses into your own areas of specialization.

Roger G. Gilbertson

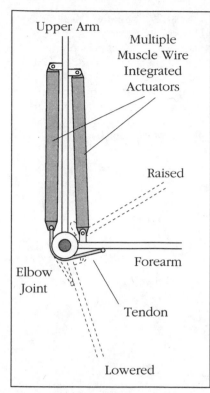

Figure 1.20   Basic Limb Joint
The basic limb joint using integrated actuators. The opposing actuators receive power and communications signals from external sources, and would provide fast, strong motion and precise control in both directions.

Figure 1.21   Integrated Actuator
This module could combine multiple Muscle Wires with sensors and control circuitry to create efficient linear motion. The high strength to weight ratio of Muscle Wires could make these devices the ideal choice for many robotic applications. Illustration by Tom Twohy.

Integrated Actuators

To increase the total force available in a Muscle Wire powered device, these basic modules would combine groups of wires with force and position sensors, thermal insulation, communication and active cooling systems (see Part Two for more on this), all in compact, flexible packages. These actuators would be the robotic equivalent of muscle groups in living creatures.

When attached to a machine skeleton, and connected to power and communication networks, groups of these actuators could create quiet, efficient linear motion, without pneumatic or hydraulic pressure sources, and without the mass and size drawbacks of motors.

The illustrations on the following pages demonstrate a few possible applications for these all-electric actuators, including prosthetic limbs, active limb braces, robot actuators, and even complete android robot systems.

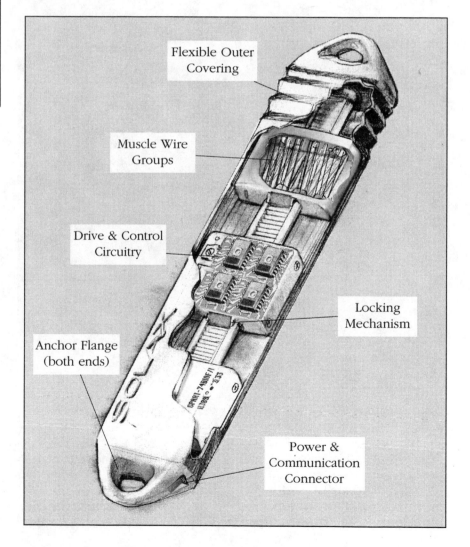

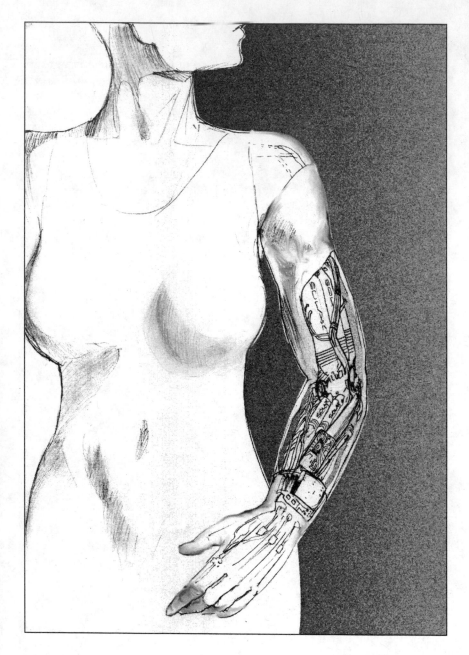

Figure 1.22 Advanced Prosthetic Arm
Powered by an advanced battery pack worn around the waist or behind the back, this artificial arm would use several Muscle Wire-driven integrated actuators and sophisticated control circuitry to provide life-like action and real-world functionality. Illustration by Tom Twohy.

Artificial Limb

Consisting of a strong, lightweight frame, several integrated actuators, coordinating electronics, and a life-like covering, this electronic limb could resemble a human arm, and provide very realistic and highly functional motion. A separate, rechargeable battery would provide power to the arm, and could be worn in a small backpack.

The user could control the arm in several ways; via sensors that detect impulses at the nerve endings, by sensors acting on signals from other muscles, or by computerized interfaces that interpret head and eye actions and convert them to arm motions.

Realistic artificial limbs are an application where the strength and compactness of Muscle Wires provide great advantages.

Roger G. Gilbertson

Active Brace with Muscle Amplifiers

Worn on the legs just like conventional braces, the active brace has sensors, amplifiers and groups of integrated Muscle Wire actuators that permit a person with reduced muscle ability to travel without a wheelchair or crutches.

The active brace would use several externally worn integrated actuators powered by an advanced battery pack worn on a belt, or even via a power cord from an AC powered recharger. Advanced balance sensors (evolved from existing devices[38]) would continuously monitor the wearer's motion and stability, and could quickly take corrective actions to prevent falls.

With some types of impairment the brace would sense and amplify the wearer's own muscle actions. For other individuals, the brace itself would generate the balance and motion patterns. Devices like the active brace could provide an alternative to the wheelchair for many mobility impaired people.

The sense-and-amplify active brace system could serve as a restrengthening tool for astronauts returning from long exposure to zero gravity, and by other persons regaining strength after long periods of muscular inactivity.

Figure 1.23 Active Brace
Using groups of all-electric Muscle Wire actuators, the active brace would sense and amplify the body's own muscle actions, or use computer-generated motions for persons without lower body muscle control. Such braces could providing new mobility to many individuals using wheelchairs, crutches, or walkers, and could assist others in rebuilding lost muscle strength. Illustration by Tom Twohy.

Future Ideas...

Teleoperated Systems

Teleoperated systems allow a user to both sense and act upon objects in distant locations, and permit people to perform work in exotic or hazardous environments from a remote location. Muscle Wires have many possible uses in current and future systems like these.

Teleoperated devices could work in space (Fig. 1.24), on the Moon, or even on other planets or in deep space (with consideration given for communication time lags). They could provide greater flexibility in mission planning, easier access to high orbits, and reduced expense and risk.

On Earth, specially shielded teleoperated devices could assist in cleaning and reconditioning toxic or contaminated sites where humans can tolerate only short periods of exposure. For working deep under water, a typical teleoperated system would have it's operator located safely aboard ship, or even on shore. These systems could permit operations in waters of extreme temperatures and pressures, under adverse weather conditions, and for extended periods of time not possible for human divers.

Other Muscle Wire devices could provide detailed tactile signals (see Fig. 1.17) and "force feedback" to the teleoperator, indicating, for example, when a remote robot hand has encountered an object, or met with resistance to its action.

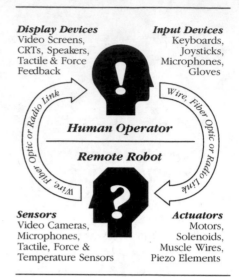

Figure 1.24 Basics of Telepresence
Teleoperated systems involve two data streams. One carries data from remote sensors to the human operator, while the other takes the operator's input and creates action at the remote system.

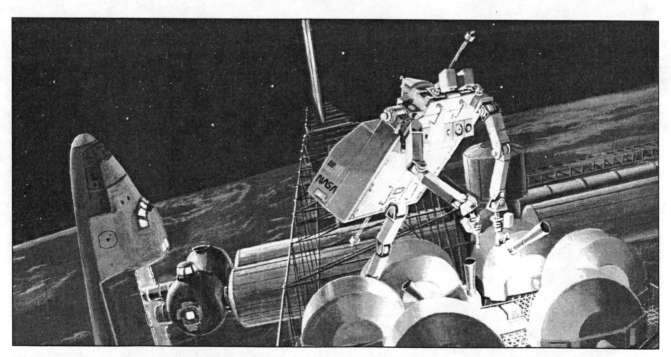

Figure 1.25 Remotely Operated "Telepresence" Robot
The Flight Telerobotic Servicer (FTS) would enable astronauts to perform routine assembly and maintenance work without leaving the Space Shuttle or Space Station.

Though not part of the FTS, similar telerobotic systems could employ Muscle Wires for actuators and to provide tactile and "force feedback" to the operator. Illustration courtesy Martin Marietta Civil Space & Communications.

Roger G. Gilbertson

Teleoperated Surgical Systems

Another area for teleoperated systems reaches neither into space nor underwater, but into the human body. Teleoperated surgical systems could greatly reduce the trauma, infection risk and hospitalization time involved in many medical procedures.

More and more, doctors perform "minimally invasive" operations using fiber optic cameras and slender tools inserted into small incisions. Such procedures include gall bladder removal, and repairing tendons in the knee or other joints.

Advanced teleoperated surgical systems would extend the surgeon's capabilities, and could use Muscle Wires in several ways. Remotely controlled micro tools would use their strength to grasp, cut and clamp. Other tools inserted into the body might include high resolution 3-D color micro cameras, lights, and laser tools.

The surgeon's gloves would also contain Muscle Wire devices. Each fingertip would rest on a tactile display device that would create physical sensations corresponding to the force, pressure or temperature encountered by the tiny remote tools. Examples include signaling when a tiny cutter contacts tissue, or indicating the pulse in an artery as measured by a remote probe.

In other circumstances, as a remote tool encounters resistance, force feedback devices in the gloves might resist the closing of the surgeon's hand.

Figure 1.26 Teleoperated Coronary Bypass Surgery
In a coronary bypass operation, the surgeon installs a new section of artery or synthetic tubing to bridge a clogged artery that supplies blood to the muscles on the surface of the heart in order to restore full blood flow. Currently, the rib cage must be cut open and spread apart to permit the surgeon's hands inside. Using advanced teleoperated tools, this operation might be performed using a much smaller incision below the ribs, with cameras, lights and remote tools such as the SMA driven "microhands" as shown here, inserted under the rib cage to the heart. The surgeon's visor would display a 3-D color image of the operating area, and the gloves would contain position sensors as well as Muscle Wire force and tactile feedback devices to let the surgeon precisely feel the action of the remote tools inside the patient's body. Illustration by Tom Twohy.

Autonomous Robots

Advances in computers, machine intelligence and mobile power sources may someday make possible autonomous robots capable of performing a wide range of tasks. Rather than replacing human skills and intelligence, these machines would be well suited to perform tasks too repetitive, dangerous or even impossible for humans.

Robots like the *robocrab* in Figure 1.27 would create entirely new possibilities for design and construction of large scale structures. These machines might use a form of the *subsumption* software developed by Rodney Brooks and Anita Flynn at the Massachusetts Institute of Technology.[39] This control architecture permits simple machines to not only exhibit complex behavior but also perform "real world" tasks.

Rather than deciding the activity of the robot as a whole, the subsumption program defines the functions for each part (joint, foot, sensor, etc.) and how it responds both to other parts, and to the external world in various situations. The robots do not contain an internal "model" of the world (as with many artificial intelligence methods) but instead, use many sensors to directly "read" the real world since it "is a rather good model of itself."[40]

Groups of autonomous robots could perform complex tasks, and might form a kind of mechanical ecology with various machines filling specialized niches. Advanced robocrabs might even perform maintenance on each other, and could reproduce by building duplicates of themselves given the basic component parts.

Fig. 1.27   Construction and Maintenance "Robocrabs"
Small, autonomous, Muscle Wire driven robots could climb, haul, cut, clamp, weld, and perform many other functions. They could work as automatic tools for assembling large, complex structures, such as gigantic domes and floating spheres based on the extremely lightweight and strong tensegrity structures proposed and developed by R. Buckminster Fuller. Illustration by Tom Twohy.

Fig. 1.28 Spherecraft

An aluminum and polyester sphere 1,600 meters in diameter and weighing 5,400 metric tons, when heated by the sun, displaces enough air that it becomes buoyant and can float in the atmosphere just as a steel ship floats in the ocean.[41] This huge *aerostat* could hover at 30 km above the surface and serve as an earth, ocean and atmosphere monitoring and research station, solar power relay, or long range communications platform. The structure would contain over 2.2 million struts and could be assembled and maintained by teams of Muscle Wire driven robots, and might even contain shape memory alloy "smart material" components in its structure. Illustration: Archives of the Buckminster Fuller Institute.[42]

Robocrabs might one day build large, lightweight, freestanding domes that protect architectural and archeological sites, provide controlled weather conditions for farms or towns, or cover highly contaminated sites to prevent spreading during clean up.

Containing millions of parts joined in a regular pattern, giant *tensegrity spheres* (Fig. 1.28) represent the kind of large scale engineering well suited to construction by teams of autonomous robots.

Specialized robots could perform construction, maintenance, digging, demolition, surveying, exploration, clean up and other tasks either difficult or dangerous for humans, and could do so reliably without human supervision. Solar powered robots could be sent to the moon or Mars to prepare sites for the later arrival of humans.[43]

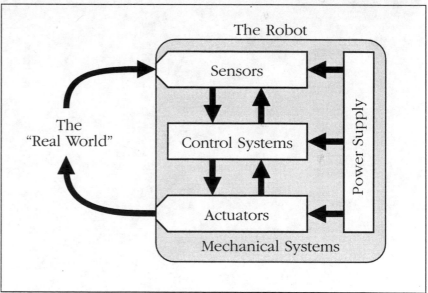

Fig. 1.29 Components of "Real World" Robotic Systems

This diagram shows the components of any robotic system designed to operate in the "real world". Sensors provide input from the external world to the control system, which operates the actuators such as motors and Muscle Wire devices to, in turn, respond to and influence the world. The power supply provides energy to the sensors, actuators and control system, and the mechanical systems include all supporting parts and structures. With increasingly sophisticated control systems, robots might someday act like insects, or even as complexly as human beings.

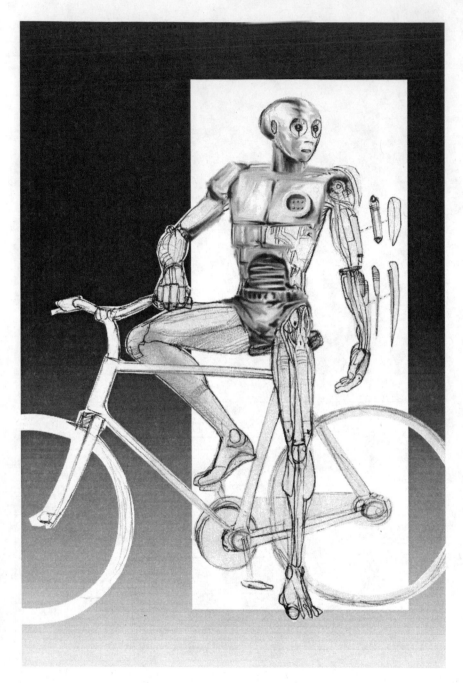

Fig. 1.30   SLRG the Android
Even with a sophisticated body, robotic machines will have limited functionality without sophisticated brains. This fully Muscle Wire driven android, named *SLRG* (after his inventors Stan, Loraine, Roy and Gary), manages to get into a large amount of trouble. Since first activation, SLRG has become an expert in corporate law, taken control of several international companies, and now travels the globe, bicycling, trading in metals and electricity, and writing travel journals full of observations about human beings. Portrait by Tom Twohy.

Android Robots

Of course, the ultimate goal of many robotics dreamers lies in the creation of human-like, or *android*, robots. For years, science fiction writers and filmmakers have presented all kinds of robots. In fact, in the 1920's the playwright Karl Čapek coined the word *robot* from the Czech word for "drudge work".

Metropolis, *The Day the Earth Stood Still*, Issac Asimov's *I, Robot*, *2001: A Space Odyssey* and *Star Wars*; these stories capture people's imaginations and set expectations for how robots should look, function and behave. But the robots built thus far all fall short of fulfilling the dreams of print and film.

For future robotic machines to reach these expectations and to perform human tasks in human environments will require computer "brains" far better than those yet developed, as well as great advances in robot mechanisms. Shape memory alloy components could perform many functions in these advanced robots.

The integrated actuators, artificial limbs, tactile displays, and teleoperated devices presented on the previous pages could be part of many sophisticated robots. Although much work and many new discoveries remain before we create such machines, storytellers and dreamers will continue to envision intelligent, android robots.

And when we finally do succeed, these human-like machines, like all our tools, will probably change us as much as they allow us to change our universe.

PART TWO

All About Muscle Wires

This section describes the basic properties of Muscle Wires including their composition, size, forces, electrical and thermal considerations, activation speeds, and methods of working with them. Many properties vary greatly with the wire's composition and size.

Properties of Muscle Wires

Most nickel-titanium (or *nitinol)* alloys contain nearly equal atomic amounts (equal numbers of atoms, not equal weights) of nickel and titanium. Differences of less than one percent, or contaminants like iron or oxygen, can change the transition temperatures by as much as 200°C. Therefore the materials require very careful formulation and processing.

Figure 2.1 shows the steps involved in making nitinol. The manufacturer carefully measures the component metals and melts them in a vacuum furnace at 1300°C. The cast ingot is cooled, then rolled and formed into bars, rods, sheets, or most commonly, wires.

Hobbyists and experimenters most frequently use memory alloys in wire form, as they are easily cut, connected, and can be activated electrically. Bars, rods and sheets are less common, since even a simple task such as drilling a hole in a bar of nitinol presents a challenge: the friction from the spinning drill bit heats the metal and causes it to transform to the much harder form.

Nitinol's hardness (greater than some steels) and its shape changing abilities makes processing difficult and expensive. Grinding, etching, EDM (electric discharge machining) and laser cutting are other methods used to fabricate SMA parts. A piece of nitinol can be made to "remember" a

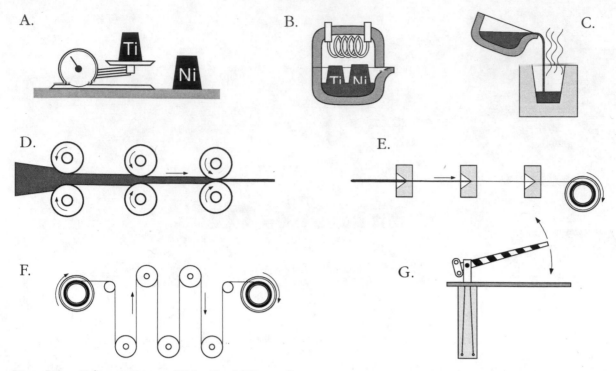

Figure 2.1   Making, Training and Using Muscle Wires

To make Muscle Wires, equal parts of nickel and titanium are measured (A), melted together (B), then cast into a solid ingot (C). The ingot is heated, rolled and formed (D), then drawn through a series of dies (E) to obtain the desired diameter. Wires are then annealed and trained on cycling equipment (F). Finally, the end user employs the wires to create motion in a device (G) that, if properly designed, will maintain the wire's memory and longevity.

shape by forming it at low temperature to the desired shape, clamping it solidly to prevent it from moving, and heating it past its transformation temperature to its annealing temperature at around 540°C.

When cooled, the shape can be easily deformed, and when heated, it will return to the annealed form. Muscle Wires' carefully controlled annealing and pretraining gives them nearly unlimited lifetimes when used in devices that protect them from overstressing (too much force), overstraining (too much stretching) and overheating (temperatures too far above the alloy's transition temperature).

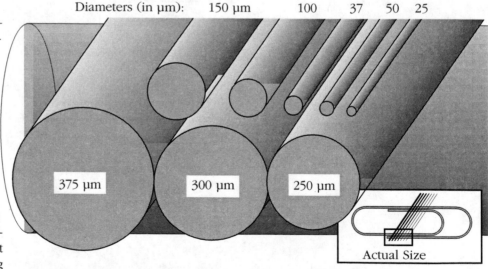

Figure 2.2   Muscle Wires – Small and Strong
Some typical Muscle Wire diameters, as compared to a paper clip. The wires are very strong for their small size. Wires are measured in micrometers (µm, also called microns). 1000 µm = 1 mm. Shown 100 times actual size.

Density — *The measure of the amount of matter in a given volume. For nitinol, about 6.45 grams per cubic centimeter. (Water = 1 g/cc).*

Diameter

Very small wires are measured in micrometers (µm - thousandths of a millimeter). Typical human hairs measure from 25 to 100 µm in diameter, Muscle Wires range from 25 to 375 µm. A wire's diameter directly affects many parameters including its resistance per unit length, the force needed to deform it (when cool), the force it exerts on its recovery (when heated), the maximum force it can withstand before breaking, the cooling rate (small wires cool faster than large ones), and the minimum bend radius. This section gives additional information.

Diameter — *The measure of a wire's cross-sectional width, given in micrometers (µm). See Figure 2.3.*

Forces

Nitinol shape memory alloys can exert as much as 600 million newtons per square meter — that's over 40 tons per square inch! The force exerted by a wire depends on its composition, size and training. Larger wires will exert more force than small ones having the same composition and training. Figure 2.3 gives the equations for calculating dimensions relating to a wire's length and diameter.

The following are some other terms relating to forces and Muscle Wires. For each of these forces, multiply the given value by a wire's cross-sectional area to get the force for that wire.

Maximum Recovery Force — *The largest force a wire will exert when heated. For nitinol this is about 600 MPa (megapascal or million Newtons per square meter).*

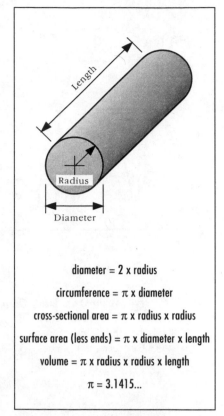

diameter = 2 x radius

circumference = π x diameter

cross-sectional area = π x radius x radius

surface area (less ends) = π x diameter x length

volume = π x radius x radius x length

π = 3.1415...

Figure 2.3   Equations Relating to Diameter and Cross-sectional Area

Minimum Bend Radius

Minimum bend radius describes the smallest bend a Muscle Wire can make without risking damage. Avoid sharp bends or kinks as they can overstrain and weaken a wire (Figure 2.5).

As a rule, do not bend a wire around a radius tighter than fifty times its diameter. For example, a 100 µm diameter wire can bend around a 5000 µm (equal to 5 mm) radius (or 10 mm diameter) pulley wheel. This table gives examples for some common wire diameters.

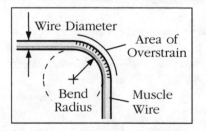

Figure 2.5   Minimum Bend Radius

Wire Diameter	Min. Bend Radius
25 µm	1.25 mm
37 µm	1.85 mm
50 µm	2.50 mm
75 µm	3.75 mm
100 µm	5.00 mm
125 µm	6.25 mm
150 µm	7.50 mm
200 µm	10.00 mm
250 µm	12.50 mm
300 µm	15.00 mm
375 µm	18.75 mm

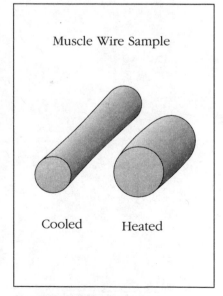

Figure 2.4   Wire Expansion
As a wire heats and shortens it also increases in diameter (exaggerated above). The action of this expansion can be used for very small motions and microscopic actuators.

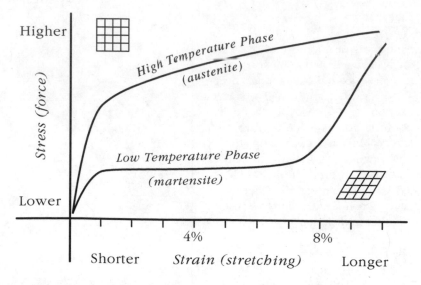

Figure 2.6 Typical Stress vs. Strain Curve for Shape Memory Alloys
A typical stress-versus-strain curve for a shape memory alloy, showing the difference between the low temperature (or *martensite*) phase and the high temperature (or *austenite*) phase.

Recommended Recovery Force
— *The force recommended for use with Muscle Wires to protect and preserve their factory training, usually about one-third of the Maximum Recovery Force, or about 200 MPa for nitinol.*

Recommended Bias Force —
The bias force that should be applied to extend or deform a cooled Muscle Wire. It is usually one tenth to one twentieth of the Maximum Recovery Force, or from 30 to 60 MPa.

Figure 2.7 Mass, Weight and Force
The standard U.S. one cent coin has a mass of 2.50 grams and exerts a force of 0.0245 Newtons at the Earth's surface. (Force in Newtons equals mass in kilograms times 9.8 (or if in grams, times 0.0098), the acceleration of gravity at sea level.

The projects in Part Three of this book use groups of one cent coins pulled by the earth's gravity to generate various forces.

Recovery Ratios

These ratios compare the deformed (cooled) and contracted (heated) lengths of a Muscle Wire and indicate how much motion to expect.

Maximum Recovery Ratio (or Recovery Strain) — *A percentage expressing the largest strain (change in length or stretch) to expect from a wire (about 8% for nitinol). Most wires can perform for only a few cycles at maximum deformation.*

Recommended Recovery Ratio — *A percentage expressing the recommended strain (change in length or stretch) for maximum wire life and repeated performance (3 to 5% for nitinol wires).*

Breaking Strength — *The force a wire can withstand before breaking. It varies with wire diameter, composition, temperature and processing. For nitinol, about ten times the maximum recovery force, or 1000 MPa (71 ton / in²). Expect deformation of 15 to 30% before breakage.*

Superelasticity — *A property of SMAs where, in the high temperature (austenite) phase, the metal can be stretched or deformed much more than most metals, without causing permanent damage to the metal's crystal structure. Alloys having transition temperatures below "room temperature" (20°C) are superelastic at room temperature and above.*

Young's Modulus — *For most materials this is a constant describing a material's ability to endure strain (changes in length). But for SMAs, Young's Modulus varies greatly with composition, elongation, training and temperature. For nitinol in the low temp phase it is around 28 Gigapascal (like lead) and in the high temp phase it is around 75 GPa (like aluminum). See Figure 2.8.*

Roger G. Gilbertson

Properties	Flexinol Name	025	037	050	075	100	125	150	200	250	300	375
Physical	Wire Diameter (μm)	25	37	50	75	100	125	150	200	250	300	375
	Minimum Ben Radius (mm)	1.3	1.85	2.5	3.75	5.0	6.25	7.5	10.0	12.50	15.0	18.75
	Cross-sectional Area (μm²)	490	1,075	1,960	4,420	7,850	12,270	17,700	31,420	49,100	70,700	110,450
Electrical	Linear Resistance (Ω/m)	1,770	860	510	200	150	70	50	31	20	13	8
	Recommended Current[†] (mA)	20	30	50	100	180	250	400	610	1,000	1,750	2,750
	Recommended Power[†] (W/m)	0.71	0.78	1.28	2.0	4.86	4.4	8.00	12.0	20.0	39.8	60.5
Strength	[*]Max. Recovery Weight @ 600 MPa (g)	29	65	117	250	469	736	1,056	1,860	2,933	4,240	6,630
	Rec. Recovery Weight @ 190 MPa (g)	7	20	35	80	150	230	330	590	930	1,250	2,000
	Rec. Deformation Weight @ 35 MPa (g)	2	4	8	815	28	43	62	110	172	245	393
Speed	Typical Contraction Speed[††] (sec)	1.0	1.0	1.0	1.0	1.0	1.0	1.0	1.0	1.0	1.0	1.0
	LT Relaxation Speed[††] (sec)	0.16	0.25	0.3	0.5	0.8	1.6	2.0	3.5	5.5	8.0	13.0
	LT Alloy Thermal Cycle Rate (cyc/min)	52	48	46	40	33	23	20	13	9	7	4
	HT Relaxation Speed[††] (sec)	n.a.	0.09	0.1	0.2	0.4	0.9	1.2	2.2	3.5	6	10
	HT Alloy Thermal Cycle Rate (cyc/min)	n.a.	55	55	50	43	32	27	19	13	9	5

Thermal		LT Alloy	HT Alloy
	Activation Start Temp. (°C)	68	88
	Activation Finish Temp. (°C)	78	98
	Relaxation Start Temp. (°C)	52	72
	Relaxation Finish Temp. (°C)	42	62
	Annealing Temp. (°C)	300	300
	Melting Temp. (°C)	1,300	1,300
	Specific Heat (cal/g°C)	0.077	0.077
	Heat Capacity (Joule/g°C)	0.32	0.32
	Latent Heat (Joule/g)	24.2	24.2

Material			
	Density (g/cc)	6.45	
	Maximum Recovery Force (MPa)	600	(~43 ton / in²)
	Recommended Deformation Force (MPa)	35	(~2.5 ton / in²)
	Breaking Strength (MPa)	1,000	(~71 ton / in²)
	Poisson's Ratio	0.33	
	Work Output (Joule/g)	1	
	Energy Conversion Efficiency (%)	5	
	Maximum Deformation Ratio (%)	8	
	Recommended Deformation Ratio (%)	3-5	

Phase Related	Phase	Martensite	Austenite
	Resistivity (μΩcm)	76	82
	Young's Modulus (GPa)	28	75
	Magnetic Susceptibility (μemu/g)	2.5	3.8
	Thermal Conductivity (W/cm°C)	0.08	0.18

[†] In still air, at 20°C.

[*] To obtain force in Newtons, multiply mass in grams by 0.0098.

[††] Depends greatly on local heating and cooling conditions. See text.

Figure 2.8 Flexinol Muscle Wire Properties
This table shows values for various sizes of Flexinol Muscle Wires that have a transition temperature of 70°C.

Poisson's Ratio — *Describes how much a material narrows when pulled at each end (i.e. the cross-sectional shrinkage in a material under strain). For nitinol it is about 0.33 (the same as aluminum). Like Young's Modulus, this ratio varies widely, and depends greatly on the alloy's composition, training and temperature.*

Magnetic Fields & Susceptibility
Nitinol is virtually non magnetic. Also a straight wire carrying a current generates a much smaller magnetic field than does a coil of wire (as in motors and solenoids).

Electrical Properties

Voltage, current, and resistance of a Muscle Wire follow the basic equation of electricity, Ohm's Law:

$$V = i \times R$$

voltage (in volts) equals current (in amps) times resistance (in ohms)

So if you know a wire's resistance (which varies directly with its length) and the recommended current level to activate it, you can calculate the required voltage by using Ohm's Law. For example, a 10 cm

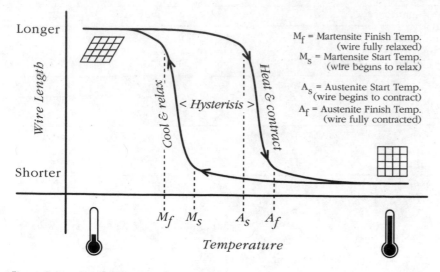

M_f = Martensite Finish Temp.
(wire fully relaxed)
M_s = Martensite Start Temp.
(wire begins to relax)

A_s = Austenite Start Temp.
(wire begins to contract)
A_f = Austenite Finish Temp.
(wire fully contracted)

Figure 2.9   Muscle Wire Length vs. Temperature
This graph shows the behavior of a Muscle Wire under a constant force. As the wire heats, its contraction follows the right-hand curve. When the temperature reaches A_s the wire has started to shorten. When it reaches A_f it is near full contraction, and almost all crystals have transformed to the harder austenite phase. As the wire cools, it follows the left-hand curve, starting at the lower right and passing through M_s and M_f as the crystals change to the martensite phase and the wire relaxes and lengthens.

long wire with a linear resistance of 0.5 Ω/cm (half an ohm per centimeter) has 5 Ω total resistance. With a recommended current level of 400 mA (0.400 amps), use Ohm's Law to find the voltage as follows:

$$V = i \times R$$
$$V = 0.400 \times 5 = 2.0 \text{ V}$$

or two volts, measured from end to end on the Muscle Wire.

Power, a measure of the total energy needed by a wire, is found by another simple equation:

$$W = i \times V$$

power (in watts) equals current (in amps) times voltage (in volts)

or it can also be found by:

$$W = i^2 \times R$$

power (in watts) equals current (in amps) squared times resistance (in ohms)

For example, given a wire that operates with 3 volts (measured

end to end) and with 100 milliamps of current flowing through it, the power used is:

$$W = i \times V$$
$$W = 0.100 \times 3 = 0.300 \text{ W}$$

or 300 milliwatts. Doubling the length of the wire doubles its total resistance, and also its power needs. Double the length of the wire in the above example and it will need 0.600 watts. For more on electricity and basic electronics, see the appendices and the books listed in the references section (page J-1).

The following terms concern the electrical properties of Muscle Wires:

Bulk Resistivity — *This indicates a material's opposition to electric current regardless of its shape. For nitinol this is approximately 70 μΩcm in the low temperature (martensite) phase, and 90 μΩcm in the high temperature (austenite) phase.*

Resistance *(or Linear Resistance) — This indicates a material's opposition to electric current when formed into wires, and is measured in ohms. In wire form, nitinol has a resistance per unit length determined by its bulk resistivity and diameter. Small wires have higher resistances than large wires. Figure 2.8 gives examples.*

To calculate resistance for a wire, multiply the Bulk Resistivity of the material (in μΩcm) times 10,000 (a scaling factor) and divide by the wire's cross-sectional area (in μm²). Note that due to the difficulty in measuring small wires and problems with round off errors, a better way is to measure the actual resistance of a length of wire with an ohmmeter.

Recommended Current Level — *For a Muscle Wire, this is a typical current level that will activate but*

but not quickly overheat the wire in still air at room temperature (around 20°C). This is useful as a starting point for testing new devices, but use caution — actual current needs vary due to local cooling conditions.

Temperature Properties

When a Muscle Wire carries an electric current, the metal's natural resistance causes it to dissipate part of the current as heat. This heat raises the temperature of the wire, and if it is high enough, the wire will undergo the Shape Memory Effect phase change.

The activation and relaxation temperatures for nitinol alloys can fall in the range of -200 to +110°C, depending on the formulation of the alloy. Differences of less than 1% in the ratio of the component metals greatly affect the actual transition temperature. Other shape memory alloys operate over different temperature ranges, both higher and lower.

Here are some terms relating to temperatures in Muscle Wires:

Transition Temperature — *The point where the wire changes from its easily deformed low temperature phase to its harder high temperature phase, or vice versa when cooling.*

In actual practice, the change occurs over a small temperature range and has some hysteresis (see Fig. 2.9 and page 1-2), but for general experimenting and hobby purposes it can be considered to occur "all at once".

Activation Start Temperature (Austenite Start Temp. or A_s) — *The point at which the crystals in a wire begin changing from the low*

temperature martensite phase to the high temperature austenite phase. This begins a wire's contraction and its return to a previously learned shape (the reverse transformation).

Activation Finish Temperature (Austenite Finish Temp. or A_f) — *The point at which all crystals in a wire have changed to the high temperature austenite phase. This completes a wire's contraction and the reverse transformation.*

Relaxation Start Temperature (Martensite Start Temp. or M_s) — *The point at which the crystals in a wire begin transforming from the high temperature (austenite) phase to the low temperature (martensite) phase. This begins a wire's relaxation and starts the martensite transformation.*

Relaxation Finish Temperature (Martensite Finish Temp. or M_f) — *The point at which all crystals in a wire have changed to the low temperature (martensite) phase. This completes a wire's relaxation and ends the martensite transformation.*

Temperature Hysteresis — *A difference in the starting and ending temperatures that depends on the initial condition of the wire (relaxed or contracted). Shape memory alloys have a slightly different transition temperature depending on whether the material is being heated or cooled (see Figure 2.9).*

Annealing Temperature — *For Muscle Wires, the temperature at which any residual strains are removed, and the crystal structure of the metal reforms, erasing any previous training (around 540°C for nitinol).*

When activating a Muscle Wire, use care to prevent it from overheating.

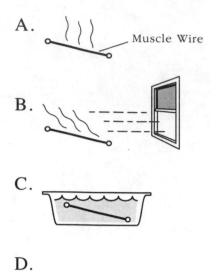

A.
Muscle Wire

B.

C.

D.

E.

F.

Figure 2.10 Heat Sink Methods
The insulating conditions surrounding a Muscle Wire can greatly affect its performance, since the faster the wire cools, the faster it will relax. Situations with different cooling rates include a Muscle Wire in still air (A), in moving air (B), in a fluid (C), inside rubber tubing (D), in a vacuum (E), and active cooling systems (F).

Even temperatures below the annealing point can cause damage to a previously trained wire and will greatly reduce wire performance. As a rule, when power is removed from an activated wire, if it does not begin to relax *almost immediately*, it has been overheated, and the power level should be reduced.

Melting Temperature — *The temperature at which a solid becomes a liquid. Nitinol alloys melt at approximately* 1300°C.

Thermal Conductivity — *The ability of a material to transfer heat energy. For nitinol this measures around 0.08 watt/cm°C in the low temperature (martensite) phase, and 0.18 watt/cm°C in the high temperature (austenite) phase.*

Speed Properties

The speed at which Muscle Wires contract and relax depends on many factors including the circuit driving the wire, the surrounding conditions, and the wire's composition. However, since the phase changes occur only when the wire reaches its transition temperature, it exerts the same force whether it is heated quickly or slowly.

When heated, a Muscle Wire can contract as fast as *one thousandth* of a second. The total time for one complete contract and relax action depends on the wire's composition, the power applied, and especially on the local cooling conditions.

The faster a Muscle Wire can be cooled, the faster its cycle time. Thin wires cool faster than thicker ones. Because of their smaller volume they have less total heat to dissipate. So, to increase strength but retain the fast speed of smaller wires, use several small wires in parallel.

Heat Sinks

To relax, an activated Muscle Wire must be cooled. The cooling rate depends greatly on the "heat sink" or the ability of the material surrounding a wire to carry away the heat. Air, liquids, coatings or other materials in contact with a wire, even crimps, can have greatly differing heat sink effects.

Still air surrounding a Muscle Wire makes the most basic heat sink (Fig. 2.10-A). Moving air will cool a wire faster (Fig. 2.10-B), and immersing it in water or a water/glycerine mixture will greatly increase the cooling rate (Fig. 2.10-C).

Running a wire through small diameter rubber tubing (Fig. 2.10-D) has a dual effect. First, the tube insulates the wire from moving air, letting it heat rapidly. Second, the rubber acts as a heat sink and helps it cool faster.

A vacuum (Fig. 2.10-E) provides a poor heat sink, as there is nothing to carry heat away except thermal radiation. Placing the Muscle Wire in contact with a thermally conductive mass (but electrically insulating) will increase the cooling rate.

Devices having many Muscle Wires can use active cooling systems to circulate a fluid medium over the wires and through a radiator (Fig. 2.10-F). Many Muscle Wire devices will operate in still air at room temperature. When first testing a device, use the Recommended Current Level (see Fig. 2.8) as a starting point, and then adjust the power level according to actual performance.

In general, a stronger heat sink (water, moving air, etc.) will cause a wire to require more power to reach its transition temperature. But use care, as higher power levels can increase the risk of overheating, which can cause permanent wire damage, and can even ignite and burn very small wires.

Cutting

Use heavy scissors or wire cutters to snip the wire. Do not use the "good scissors" as the hardness of the nickel-titanium alloy will put a nick in their edge.

Connecting

Muscle Wires increase in diameter as they shorten in length and can exert large forces on anchor points, rollers, and supporting structures. Any connection to a Muscle Wire needs two features: strength and electrical conductivity.

Because current must flow through a wire to heat it, a poor connection can greatly reduce the power level to the wire. Generally, a connection solid enough to hold the wire will also provide a good electrical connection.

Figure 2.13 shows several types of crimps and other connection methods. They include rail joiners from N scale model railroads (available at hobby stores), small electrical connectors (available at hardware stores, good for larger wires), brass and stainless steel tubing (good for very small crimps), and pieces of sheet metal (which can be formed to help attach or guide Muscle Wires in a mechanism).

Looping the Muscle Wire back through the crimp (Fig. 2.13-A) provides an even better mechanical anchor and gives twice the electrical exposure. A weak crimp will permit the wire to slip, while an overly compressed crimp may damage or overstrain the wire, encouraging it to break.

Adding a straightened staple and a small connecting wire to the crimp (Fig 2.13-B) gives a quick and easy way to anchor and connect the wire. Screws provide quick, adjustable, and reliable

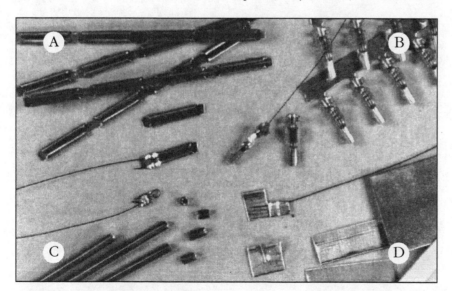

Figure 2.11 Crimps for Muscle Wires
Crimps are preferred as connectors for their convenience and strength. Many things work as crimps: model railroad rail joiners (A), small electrical connectors (B), brass or stainless steel tubing (C) and copper or brass sheets (D). A crimp must provide a solid physical anchor, and good electrical conductivity.

connections, and permit easy changing of wires. Use a threaded hole for a solid anchor point and simple adjustment, or use a screw and nut (Fig. 2.13-C).

Pinning provides a good method for direct attachment to circuit boards and mechanisms, but the wire should not make a tight bend which would weaken it over time. Drill a hole, insert the wire and press in a brass or copper pin (Fig. 2.13-D).

For adjustability, pin one end of the wire and use a screw at the other. Soldering is not recommended, as it does not hold well to the moving Muscle Wire and the heat of soldering can completely destroy a Muscle Wire's special processing.

However, when soldering a crimp to another surface, hold the wire close to the crimp with tweezers or small pliers to act as a heat sink (Fig. 2.13-E), and keep the heating time to a minimum.

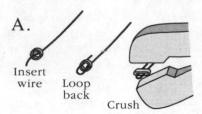

A.

Insert wire   Loop back   Crush

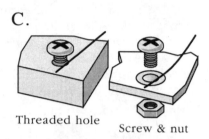

B.

With thin wire   With wire and staple

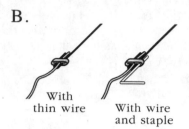

C.

Threaded hole   Screw & nut

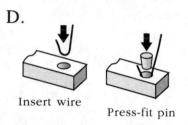

D.

Insert wire   Press-fit pin

E.

Hold the Muscle Wire with tweezers to protect it from the heat of the soldering iron

Figure 2.13 Connection Methods
Connections include crimps (A), crimps with connector and anchor wires (B), screws in a threaded hole or with a nut (C), press fit pin (D) and soldering to a crimped wire (E). However, the heat of soldering can easily damage Muscle Wires and extreme care must be used to protect the wire from overheating.

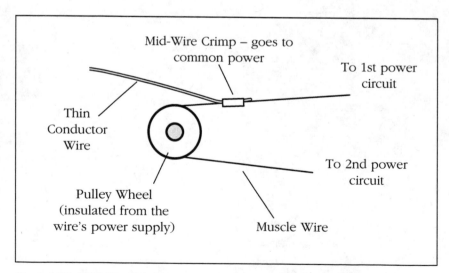

Mid-Wire Crimp – goes to common power

To 1st power circuit

Thin Conductor Wire

To 2nd power circuit

Pulley Wheel (insulated from the wire's power supply)

Muscle Wire

Figure 2.12 Mid-Wire Connection
Rollers, pins, and other points that contact a Muscle Wire should be insulated from the electrical system powering the wire. The combination of motion and electrical contact can cause sparking, oxidation, wear, and eventual breaking of the wire. If a mid-wire contact is required, attach a crimp to the wire and run a thin, flexible conductor from it to the circuit.

Roger G. Gilbertson

Efficiency

In Muscle Wires, the transformation of electricity to motion via resistance heating of a wire and the Shape Memory Effect phase change, has a low efficiency. At most, five percent of the electricity's potential for work becomes usable physical force, with 95% lost as heat. By comparison, small DC electric motors work with 30% or more efficiency in converting electricity to motion.

However, Muscle Wires often provide benefits that far outweigh their electrical inefficiency. Properties such as their high strength-to-weight ratio, large initial force, small size, direct linear motion and low operating voltages often permit devices with overall better performance than other systems, and allows for devices that would be difficult or impossible to make using motors or solenoids.

Larger Muscle Wires use power slightly more efficiently than small wires due to reduced cooling loses, but they generally have slower relaxation rates.

Lifetime

The life expectancy of Muscle Wires depend in part on their composition, processing, and training, but mostly on the operating conditions.

For Muscle Wires operating at the maximum recovery ratio (eight percent deformation), expect only a few dozen cycles. However, when used at the recommended recovery ratio of three to five percent deformation, and with proper protection from overstressing, overstraining, and overheating, the same wires can function for millions of cycles. Often, the mechanism will wear out before the Muscle Wire does!

Circuits for Muscle Wires

Circuits for Muscle Wires provide several needs; power to heat the wire and cause it to shorten, power to drive supporting circuitry, power and logic to sense and control the wire's action, and power and regulation to protect the wires from damage due to overheating.

Power Circuits

Power Circuits (Fig. 2.14) provide the electrical energy needed to activate a Muscle Wire and to operate the control and drive circuitry in a device. Electrical power can come from any number of sources: batteries, DC and AC line power, solar cells, fuel cells, generators, etc.

The projects in Part Three have examples of various types of power circuits including DC and/or battery power (Projects 1-9), direct AC power (Project 10), and battery or solar power (Project 12).

Refer to each of these projects for further details on these various kinds of power circuits.

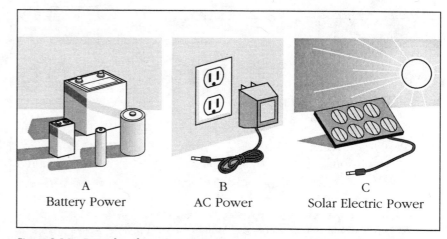

A	B	C
Battery Power	AC Power	Solar Electric Power

Figure 2.14 Examples of Power Sources
Sources of electricity for operating Muscle Wire projects and their electronics include regular and rechargeable batteries (A), DC and AC power (B), and solar electric panels (C).

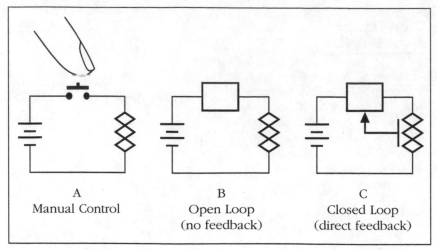

Figure 2.15   Examples of Control Circuits
Manual control circuits (A) use a human to "close the loop". Open loop control circuits (B) run a wire without feedback from it or the device it operates. Closed loop circuits (C) use sensors to regulate the action of the wire or mechanism.

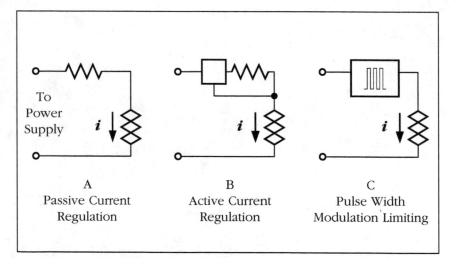

Figure 2.16   Examples of Driver Circuits
Passive driver circuits (A) use a resistor to limit the current flow. Active drivers (B) use circuitry and a power resistor to regulate the current flow, and pulse width modulation drivers (C) rapidly turn the power to the wire on and off to control the average current. Arrow "i" indicates the controlled current through the wire.

Control Circuits

Control Circuits (Fig. 2.15) regulate when and how a Muscle Wire activates. Control circuits range from simple to complex. A simple control circuit may have just a push button switch, with the operator's hand, eye and brain providing the rest of the decision making.

Other control circuits can automatically cycle on and off (Project 6), activate a wire based on an input signal (Projects 9 and 11), or have a computer program accepting information from sensors and activating wires in response (Project 14).

Driver Circuits

Driver Circuits (Fig. 2.16) provide proper levels of power to Muscle Wires, control their contraction or relaxation, and protect them from overheating. In Muscle Wire devices, driver circuits are activated and regulated by control circuits and receive power from power circuits.

Passive circuits (Fig. 2.16-A) limit current with a fixed resistor or other device to "burn up" any power not needed in the Muscle Wire. These circuits use power inefficiently, but generally have the simplest design. For an example of a passive circuit see Project 6.

Active current regulators (Fig. 2.16-B) provide a constant current for any length of Muscle Wire (limited by the size of the power supply). Like passive circuits, they "burn up" excess power. The resistor determines the current level, and the voltage regulator adjusts its output to maintain a constant current appropriate for different wire lengths. For an example, refer to the constant current circuit in Project 9.

Pulse width modulation or PWM circuits (Fig. 2.16-C) rapidly turn the current flow on and off to regulate the average power flowing through a Muscle Wire. They use power very efficiently and work well with battery or solar powered devices because of their low average current level. The circuit in Project 12 is an example of a PWM driver.

Other specialized driver circuits can power very long Muscle Wires, multiple wires, or switch between groups of wires. They may automatically lock and unlock Muscle Wire groups in order to reduce power usage, or may carefully and precisely control the action and position of a Muscle Wire, as in a radio control servo mechanism or a pointer under a microscope.

Here are examples of other specialized driver circuits:

Slow Activation — *Starts with a low power level that slowly increases but does not overheat the wire.*

Rapid Activation — *Sends a large current through the wire very quickly for fast activation, then a low current at a steady rate to hold the wire without overheating it.*

Holding Activation — *Maintains proper current levels for full activation of a wire despite changing cooling conditions, often with the help of a position sensor.*

Slow Relaxation — *Gradually reduces the current level, relaxing the wire at a desired a rate.*

Rapid Relaxation — *Requires an active heat sink like moving air, a fluid, or other material that contacts the Muscle Wire. Because of the greater heat sink, the wire requires more power for initial activation.*

Mechanisms for Muscle Wires

Mechanisms for Muscle Wires take advantage of the their ability to contract with a usable force. They transform the wire's changing shape into a usable action. Muscle Wire mechanisms can create many different actions including linear, rotating, intermittent, and combinations.

Hobbyists and experimenters can build mechanisms for robots, science fair projects, model railroads, rocketry, magic illusions, radio controlled vehicles, motion picture special effects, virtual reality systems, motorless display animation and dozens of other uses.

Part Three of this book shows examples of many of these devices and how to construct them. Many systems that use pulleys and other simple machines can give ideas for additional devices.

Also, living creatures with their contracting muscles make excellent models for efficient use of linear forces. Observe how insects and other animals operate to gain a better understanding of some of the best designs available using direct linear contractions.

Slop

Muscle Wires change shape by a relatively small amount — generally from 3 to 5 percent of their length. To make the most of their action, always adjust the wire to minimize slop (slack or looseness) when the wire is relaxed, so when the wire starts to contract it will be ready to move the mechanism.

Also, minimize wobble on pulleys, lever arms and pivots. These forms of slop also waste motion.

Bias Force Mechanisms

Generally, bias force mechanisms provide a force that opposes the contraction of a Muscle Wire. When the wire cools and relaxes, the bias helps the device return to just the starting position, but no further.

A bias force can be provided by a spring, a rubber band, a weight pulled by gravity, a magnet, even an opposing Muscle Wire.

Gravity (Fig. 2.17-A) holds constant over the wire's contraction range and provides an even force directly proportional to the hanging mass.

A spring (Fig. 2.17-B) increases its opposition force as it is pulled. The force of the magnet (Fig. 2.17-C) decreases with distance, and two opposing Muscle Wires (Fig. 2.17-D) can provide bias forces for each other, but both wires should never be powered at the same time.

In a regular or forward bias device, as the Muscle Wire contracts, the device exerts a constant or increasing force on the wire. In a *reverse bias device* the force exerted on the Muscle Wire by the mechanism *decreases* as the wire contracts (Fig.

2.17-E). This reduction in force helps to greatly extend the Muscle Wire's lifetime.

The magnet (Fig. 2.17-C) acts with a reverse bias, and both the saddle mechanism (Project 4) and the marble roller (Project 8) give additional examples. Reverse bias mechanisms are the preferred method for maximizing wire lifetimes.

The projects in Part Three give many examples of these and other bias force mechanisms.

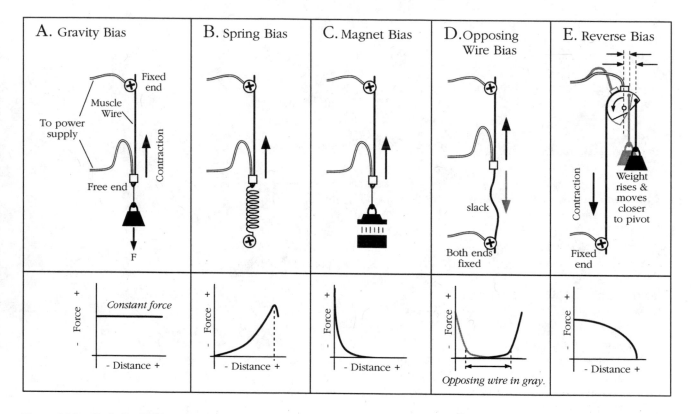

Figure 2.17   Methods of Making Bias Forces

Here are the main ways to create bias forces against Muscle Wires. When gravity pulls on the weight, it exerts a constant force *F* on the wire, which shows as the horizontal line on the graph (A). A spring or elastic band provides a steadily increasing force against the shortening Muscle Wire, up to the point where it exceeds the wire's force or where the spring fails (vertical dashed line) (B). The force of the magnet on the wire starts very strong, then drops rapidly after just a short distance (C). This is a form of reverse bias like in example E. With opposing Muscle Wires one wire can contract with little opposition until it takes up all slack and deformation length of the other wire, then the opposing force increases (D). The arrow shows the range of action. In reverse bias systems, as the Muscle Wire contracts, the force the mechanism exerts on the wire decreases. Here, it turns a cam, lifting a weight, which swings closer to the pivot, and reduces the force on the wire (E). This is the preferred way to prolong Muscle Wire lifetimes.

Muscle Wire Projects

This section contains a variety of projects that use Muscle Wires to create motion in different mechanical devices. Each project demonstrates a specific method or unique aspect of using Muscle Wire, and parts from separate examples can be combined to create many additional projects.

Project Systems

In one form or another, each of the fifteen projects contains all five of the following systems:

1. Power System — provides energy to heat the Muscle Wire and operate the control system.

2. Control System — determines when and how to apply power to the Muscle Wire.

3. Driver System — activates the Muscle Wire and protects it from overheating.

4. Muscle Wire — creates motion.

5. Mechanism — converts the Muscle Wire's contraction into motion, and protects the Muscle Wire from stress.

When powered, the Muscle Wire shortens and causes a part of the device to change position. Many different devices are possible, and the following projects illustrate a few basic mechanisms that have a wide range of applications.

The fifteen projects are presented generally in order of increasing complexity. The more involved projects should be attempted only after you have gained some experience in working with Muscle Wires, and understand the basic principles demonstrated in projects one through five.

Materials & Assembly

Many projects that demonstrate basic Muscle Wire principles can be quickly and easily built using common, easy to use materials like cardboard, tape and rubber bands. More durable and reliable devices can be built using better construction methods and stronger materials such as metal and plastic.

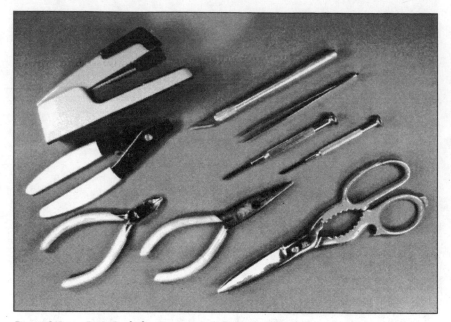

Figure 3.1   Basic Tools for Constructing the Projects
Tools include: hobby knife, tweezers, screw drivers, scissors, needle nose pliers, side cutters, wire strippers, stapler and staples. You will also require a soldering iron, solder, and related tools for the electronic portions of the projects.

Figure 3.2   Basic Materials for Constructing the Projects
Materials include: plastic sheet (acrylic, styrene and mylar of various sizes), card stock, cardboard (thin, thick and corrugated), brass tubing, batteries, coins (for weights), clear and masking tape, elastic, rubber bands, tacks, push pins, wire wrap wire, hook up wire, and thin wire from a speaker or solenoid coil. Also, the electronic circuits require various components as listed with each project.

For assembly, most of the projects require only basic hand tools like a drill, hand saw, scissors, pliers, screw drivers, wire cutters, etc. (Fig. 3.1). Some projects work best if clamped in a table vice or supported in a similar way.

For building the electronic circuits you will need a soldering iron, solder, a moist sponge, needle nose pliers, side cutters, etc. Fine tweezers can be very helpful for handling the thin Muscle Wires. If possible, use plastic tweezers to prevent nicking the wires. A hands-free magnifying glass can help with threading wires into small holes.

For the mechanical portions of the projects you will need materials like paper, corrugated cardboard (from old boxes), medium and thin cardboard (cereal boxes, recipe cards), thin plastic (mylar or acetate), thick plastic (acrylic or styrene sheet) and assorted connectors, tapes, and glues (Fig. 3.2).

The references section in the appendix lists general electronics suppliers, and each project lists sources for special items. You can also use other parts that you have available, as appropriate.

For connecting Muscle Wires to the circuits, use a thin, solid conductor such as #30 wire wrap wire. Very thin wire can be found in old speaker or microphone coils. Unwrap it and gently scrape the enamel insulation from the end before crimping.

To create various forces when testing Muscle Wire devices the projects use the standard U.S. one cent coin (copper penny) each of which has a mass of 2.50 grams.

Circuit Construction

To construct the electronic circuits you will need the components listed for each project, power supplies, wire, enclosures, etc. If you are unfamiliar with electronic assembly methods, see "Soldering Electronics" (page C-1), and the references starting on page J-1.

In building these circuits, you may choose from any of the common techniques, each suited to different needs. The breadboard method (Fig. 3.3-A) is good for temporary circuits and for testing different component values for an experimental circuit. Wire wrap (Fig. 3.3-B) is ideal for circuits with many connections and low voltage signals such as the microprocessor board in Project 14.

Perf board soldering (Fig. 3.3-C) is good for "permanent" construction and for making a single copy of a board. Printed circuit boards (Fig. 3.3-D) are ideal for assembling many copies of the same circuit.

Testing

When testing a newly completed Muscle Wire project, start with a current at or below the Recommended Current Level (see page 2-5 and 2-6) and increase it slowly until the device performs as desired.

Before operating a completed device with an untested circuit, first run the circuit separately with a "dummy load" resistor having the same resistance as the Muscle Wire. Measure the voltage and current on this resistor to determine that the circuit functions properly. This will prevent damaging or destroying a completed device, and save you much cursing and hair pulling.

And when first running a new Muscle Wire device, be prepared to unpower it quickly should it move in a unexpected or undesired way. With all construction and testing, be sure to employ appropriate safety measures. Use eye protection and observe appropriate safety precautions when soldering, operating power tools and working with high voltages.

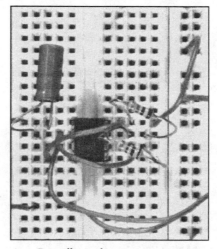

A.   Breadboard

B.   Wire Wrap

C.   Perf Board

D.   Printed Circuit Board

Figure 3.3   Circuit Assembly Techniques
Electronic circuit assembly methods include breadboard (A), wire wrap (B), perf board (C), and printed circuit board (D). Some projects may use a combination of these techniques, as each method has its own advantages.

Six Key Ideas

The following presents a review of six important rules to remember when working with Muscle Wires. They will help you get the best performance out of your Muscle Wire projects. Keep them in mind when building the projects in this book.

1. Connect Securely

Securely crimp the Muscle Wire or catch it under a screw to create an adjustable connection.

Avoid soldering Muscle Wires since heat can easily destroy the wire's unique abilities. (Page 2-9)

2. Limit Stressing

Use the correct size Muscle Wire for the intended load so that it does not have to exert more than its recommended recovery force. For longest lifetime use the wires with one-third of the Maximum Recovery Force, and a 3 to 5 percent deformation. Larger changes are possible but the increased strain will reduce the wire's lifetime. (Page 2-5)

For greater force, use two or more small Muscle Wires in parallel, rather that one larger wire. This provides the strength of a larger wire with the faster cooling rates of the small wires. Rather than trying to get a large contraction (6 or 8 percent) from a short wire, use a longer wire with a 3 to 5 percent change in length for better performance and longer wire life.

3. Use A Bias Force

Use a bias at or near the wire's recommended deformation force. It can come from a spring, rubber band, weight, etc., and should provide just enough force to return the wire to its starting position, but no more. (Page 2-12)

4. Limit Heating

Provide enough power to heat the wire to its transition temperature, but no more. A good rule is that when you remove power from an active wire, if the wire does not begin to relax almost immediately, it is being heated too much and you should reduce the power level, or heating time. (Page 2-7)

5. Limit Slop

Muscle Wires move a relatively small amount. To make the most of their force and action, adjust the wire for minimum looseness when relaxed. Also, minimize wobble on pulleys, levers and pivots. These forms of slop also waste the wire's force and motion. (Page 2-13)

6. Persist

Many techniques for using Muscle Wires may seem new and different. Sometimes it takes three or more tries to reach success. Mistakes happen, so design your devices for easy replacement of the wires. Have patience and persistence, and work in small steps rather than attempting big leaps (e.g. master a single joint before starting a whole hand).

*Explore,
experiment,
and enjoy!*

*I hear and I forget
I see and I remember
I do and I understand*

Chinese Proverb

PROJECT 1

Linear Action & Battery Power Circuit

In this device, a Muscle Wire, powered by a battery, lifts a weight against gravity and demonstrates the ability of Muscle Wires to contract with usable force.

Construction:

Bend two staples as shown in Figure 3.5. Thread the Muscle Wire into the crimp, doubling it back for added strength. Crimp securely in place. Insert one staple into the other end of the connector, add a connecting wire and crimp securely. Use care to not over-crimp and sever the wire, or under-crimp and leave anything loose. Repeat for the other end of the Muscle Wire.

Attach one end of the crimped wire to the cardboard with the tack or push pin. Mounting the cardboard vertically in a table vice helps makes it easier to operate. Place the coins in the plastic bag and hang it from the free end of the Muscle Wire. Hold the connecting wires to the cardboard base with tape, leaving some slack for the hanging end to move freely.

Connect to two AA batteries

Figure 3.4   Project 1, Linear Action
This project shows how a single Muscle Wire shortens and pulls when electrically heated. The bag of coins provides the bias force to help the wire extend again when cool.

Insert the two AA batteries into the battery holder as indicated by the (+) and (-) signs. Briefly touch the wires from the battery holder to the connecting wires (either end works fine). The Muscle Wire should contract by about 5 mm, lifting the weight. Remove the power immediately to prevent the wire from overheating, and watch it cool and relax to its original length.

Linear Action
Parts List

1	each	Muscle Wire, 150 μm dia, 10 cm long
2	each	Crimp (N-scale rail joiner, brass tube, etc.)
2	each	Staple, bent as shown
2	each	Thin connecting wire (#30 wire wrap wire or similar)
1	each	Tack or push pin
1	each	Cardboard Base (corrugated)
2	each	Battery, AA size
1	each	Battery Holder, 2 x AA, 3 volt
1	each	Small plastic bag
40	each	U.S. 1 cent coins (or other 100 gram mass)
		Tape

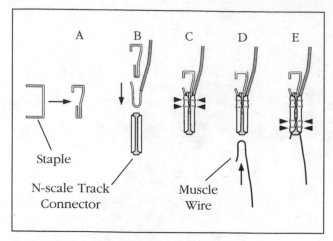

Figure 3.5   Basic Crimp and Wire Connection
Use this crimp, staple, and wire method for various projects throughout this book. N-scale track connectors for model railroads are inexpensive and easy to crimp. Bend staple (A), insert it and conductive wire into connector (B), and crimp with pliers (C). Add Muscle Wire to other end (D), and crimp it for a solid mechanical and electrical contact (E).

How it Works:

The power from the batteries flows through the Muscle Wire (see Fig. 3.6), heating it and causing it to contract and lift the coins. When power is removed, the wire cools and relaxes, and the weight pulls the wire back to its starting position.

Variations:

• With a pencil, mark the start and end points of the moving crimp on the cardboard and measure the distances. By what percentage does the wire contract?

• Blow on the wire as it relaxes. How does this change the rate at which it returns to the start position?

• This basic linear pull can be used for many devices: latches, releases, animating cardboard cut outs, moving limbs, etc.

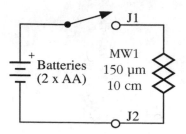

Figure 3.6   Basic Schematic
This schematic applies to Projects 1 through 4. Points J1 and J2 show where the batteries and Muscle Wire connect, and act as a switch.

PROJECT 2

Basic Lever

In this device, a length of Muscle Wire moves a lever which lifts a weight. This project shows how levers can transform the small motion of a Muscle Wire into a weaker but much larger motion.

Construction:

Assemble the Muscle Wire, crimps, staples and connecting wires as in Project 1. Photocopy the pattern sheet (page A-1) and glue it to thin cardboard (poster board or an empty cereal box). Cut out the cardboard lever for Project 2 and tack the free end of the Muscle Wire to the lever at the point labeled "W". Note that this tack points outward from the cardboard base.

Tack or push-pin the lever to the cardboard base at the point labeled "P". Position the pivot tack to take up any slack in the Muscle Wire, and so that the lever points downward to 4 o'clock. Place the coins in the bag and, using another tack pressed through from the back, hang it at the point labeled "M" (see Fig. 3.8). Tape the connecting wires to the base with slack so the lever can move freely.

Using two AA batteries in the battery holder, briefly

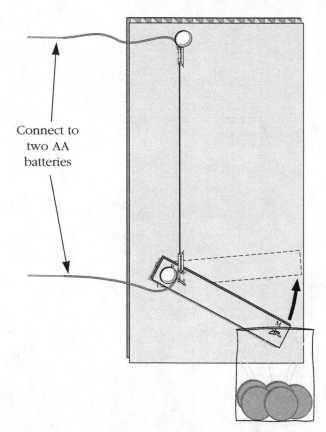

Connect to two AA batteries

Figure 3.7   Parts and Assembly for Project 2, Basic Lever
When powered, the wire contracts about 5 mm and raises the end of the lever by about 50 mm.

so the lever starts at the 1 o'clock position. How much does it move?

• Given a 10:1 lever arm, what is the largest mass that can be raised with with a 100 μm diameter Flexinol wire?

• Increase the 30 gram mass by adding one coin at a time. At what point does the device fail? What parts are likely to fail and why? How would better materials and construction help?

• Notice how the muscle in your upper arm contracts to lift your forearm. Where are the "P" and "W" points on your elbow joint? Estimate the percentage that your upper arm muscle must contract to lift your wrist by 10 cm.

• If you hold a 1 kilogram mass in your hand, how much force does it exert at the muscle (the "W" point)?

apply power to the connecting wires as in Project 1. The Muscle Wire should contract and move the lever about 30 degrees (above the 3 o'clock point). Remove power immediately and let the wire cool and relax.

How it Works:

The powered wire contracts and lifts the lever arm. Since the distance from "P" to "M" is ten times the distance "P" to the "W", the force exerted by the 30 gram mass is ten times greater at the "W" point.

The wire lifts the lever about 5 mm at the "W"

point, which becomes about ten times or 50 mm of motion at "M".

Note that multiplying the force times the lever length is an approximation that works only with the lever at or near 90° to the wire. Since the lever moves in an arc, use trigonometry to calculate its performance with other angles and positions.

Variations:

• Mark the start and end points of the lever's motion on the cardboard. Measure the distances and calculate the wire's percentage of contraction. Move the tacks

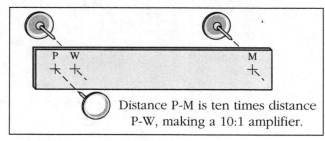

P W   M

Distance P-M is ten times distance P-W, making a 10:1 amplifier.

Figure 3.8   Lever Assembly
Note how the tacks are inserted into the cardboard arm.

• Levers convert the small change in Muscle Wire length into larger motions. Use levers in animated posters, for moving scale models, robot arms, etc.

Triangle Action

In this basic device, a length of Muscle Wires, fixed at both ends, contracts and lifts at its center. It shows how this triangular arrangement has great flexibility in converting the motion of Muscle Wires into larger motion.

Construction:

Assemble the 100 µm Muscle Wire with crimps, staples and connecting wires as in Project 1. Attach it to the cardboard base as shown in Figure 3.9 with the center of the Muscle Wire hanging down about 5 cm. Cut out the cardstock hook (Pattern Sheet page A-1) and tape it to the coins, then hang it from the Muscle Wire.

Testing:

Using two AA batteries in the battery holder, briefly apply power to the connecting wires so that it contracts and lifts the coins. Remove power immediately, and let the wire relax.

Mark the start and end point of the coins' motion, and then move one of the tacks towards or away

Triangle Action
Parts List

1	each	Muscle Wire, 100 µm dia, 10 cm long
2	each	Crimp (N-scale rail joiner, brass tube or other)
2	each	Thin connecting wire (#30 wire wrap wire or similar)
2	each	Tack or push pin
1	each	Cardboard Base (corrugated)
2	each	Battery, AA size
1	each	Battery Holder, 2 x AA, 3 volt
1	each	Small plastic bag
4	each	U.S. 1 cent coins (or other 10 gram mass)
1	each	Cardstock hook (recipe card)
		Tape

Connect to two AA batteries

Move tack to change height of triangle.

Figure 3.9   Assembly for Project 3, Triangle Action
As the Muscle Wire shortens the bottom point of the triangle rises. Moving the tacks changes the length of the triangle's base and affects how far the triangle will lift, and how strongly. The triangle geometry provides a good way of converting strength into distance.

from the other tack by about 10 mm. Repeat and observe the change in the weight's motion for various positions.

How it Works:

The Muscle Wire and hanging mass makes an inverted isosceles triangle with the base made by the line between the tacks.

The wider the base, the less deep the triangle, and the larger its change in height as the wire contracts. The appendix page

D-1 shows how to calculate the forces and distances for various triangle actuators.

Variations:

• Triangular actions are good for converting the small motion of Muscle Wires into larger motions without using levers and pivot points. Use them for latch releases, locking pins, for motion in animated posters, for moving doors, hatches, flaps, etc., on scale models, and similar applications.

Roger G. Gilbertson

PROJECT 4

Reverse Bias Saddle

In this unusual device, a length of Muscle Wire, fixed at both ends, contracts and causes a folded structure to close inward. It shows another simple way of converting the action of a Muscle Wire into a larger motion.

Construction:

Assemble the Muscle Wire, crimps, staples and connecting wires as shown in Figure 3.11. Copy the pattern sheet (page A-1) and glue it to thin cardboard (poster board or cereal box).

Cut out the cardboard saddle on the solid lines, then cut along the dotted lines and tape back in place with clear tape to form flexible hinges.

Attach the wire to the cardboard saddle, adjusting the staples so there is no slack when the saddle is slightly raised at the center as shown in Figure 3.12.

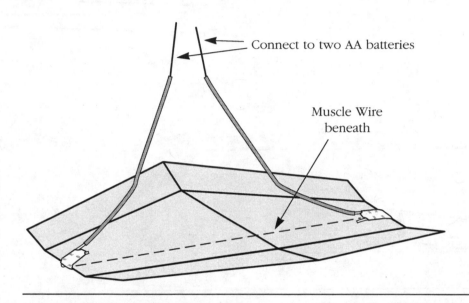

Connect to two AA batteries

Muscle Wire beneath

Figure 3.10   Project 4, The Reverse Bias Saddle
This unique shape converts the contraction of a Muscle Wire into a wide sweeping motion, with the two side flaps rising and closing inward as the wire shortens. The saddle can be built with cardboard and tape, or thin plastic for more durability.

Using two AA batteries in the battery holder, briefly apply power to the Muscle Wire. It should contract and raise the center of the saddle and pull the sides upwards. Remove power immediately to prevent overheating, and let the wire cool and relax.

How it Works:

The powered wire contracts, pulling on the saddle and causing a larger motion at its sides. As the wire contracts, the saddle folds closed and decreases the force on the wire, providing a reverse bias effect. Try closing the saddle by hand to feel the change in force it needs.

Saddle
Parts List

1	each	Muscle Wire, 150 µ m dia, 8 cm long
2	each	Crimp (N-scale rail joiner, brass tube or other)
2	each	Thin connecting wire (#30 wire wrap wire or similar)
1	each	Cardboard Saddle (per pattern)
2	each	Battery, AA size
1	each	Battery Holder, 2 x AA, 3 volt
		Tape, transparent

Figure 3.11 Saddle Assembly
Crimp the Muscle Wire at both ends, as shown. Bend the crimps to fit the cardboard saddle in it's flatter form.

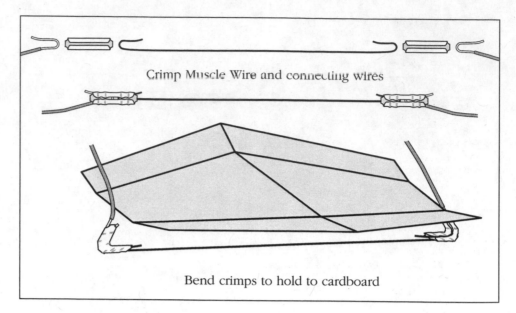

Crimp Muscle Wire and connecting wires

Bend crimps to hold to cardboard

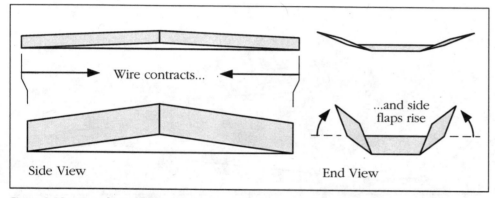

Wire contracts...

Side View

...and side flaps rise

End View

Figure 3.12 How the Saddle Moves
As the Muscle Wire shortens, it pulls on the cardboard saddle and raises the side flaps.

Variations:

• Make a more durable saddle using thin mylar or polyester sheets, and strong clear tape (like packing tape).

• Add wings to the sides of the saddle to make a simple butterfly (as in Fig. 3.13).

• Turn the saddle over (wire on top) and add eight pipe cleaners as legs for a moving spider. Having alternate legs extend underneath to the opposite side gives better balance and a more complex appearance to the motion.

• Put eyelashes on both sides of the saddle and a pupil in the center to make an eye that opens and closes.

Figure 3.13 Two Moving Bugs Using the Reverse Bias Saddle
A saddle raises the wings on a butterfly, and an inverted saddle with eight legs that alternate sides makes a kicking, jiggling spider. *Spider designed by Jeff Brown.*

PROJECT 5

Rubber Tube "Flexi" Device

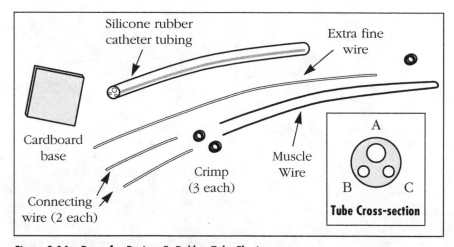

Figure 3.14   Parts for Project 5, Rubber Tube Flexi
The Muscle Wire is threaded through the two smaller holes (B and C on inset) of the small silicone tube, and the connecting wire passes through the large hole (A on inset). The three crimps attach the Muscle Wire to the thin conducting wires, and the cardboard provides an anchor for all the wires (see also Fig. 3.16).

In this device, a Muscle Wire threaded through a thin rubber tube contracts to move the tube in a unique and life-like way that resembles a finger or tentacle. By connecting the Muscle Wire at both ends, and its center, it can be made to contract and move in three directions.

Construction:

The thin silicone rubber catheter tubing can be purchased from hospital supply companies.

If you use extra fine wire from a speaker or microphone you must gently scrape the enamel insulation from its end before crimping.

Start by crimping the Muscle Wire and the extra fine wire together at the *center* of the Muscle Wire. Pass the two ends of the Muscle Wire through the small holes in the tubing, and the extra fine wire down the large hole (Fig. 3.16).

Attach crimps to the ends of the Muscle Wire and fit the tube into the slot on the cardboard square, placing one crimp on either side. Pull on the crimps to take up any slack in the Muscle Wire until the tube just starts to bend, and tape the crimps securely to the cardboard as shown in Figure 3.16.

Using two AA batteries in the battery holder, briefly apply power to any two of the three connecting wires. The Muscle Wire should contract and pull the tubing over. Remove power immediately to prevent the wire from overheating, and watch the wire cool and relax.

Flexi Parts List

1	each	Surgical catheter tube, 3 hole, 6 cm long (see text)
1	each	Muscle Wire, 100 μm dia, 13 cm long
2	each	Crimp (small brass tube or other)
3	each	Thin connecting wire (#30 wire wrap wire or similar)
1	each	Extra fine wire (taken from an old speaker coil or AC power cord)
1	each	Cardboard square
2	each	Battery, AA size
1	each	Battery Holder, 2 x AA, 3 volt
		Tape, clear

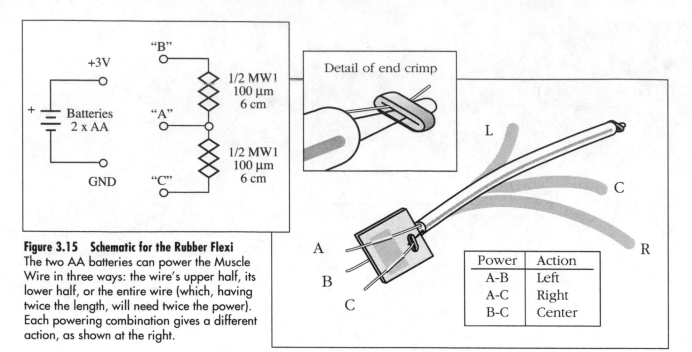

Figure 3.15 Schematic for the Rubber Flexi
The two AA batteries can power the Muscle Wire in three ways: the wire's upper half, its lower half, or the entire wire (which, having twice the length, will need twice the power). Each powering combination gives a different action, as shown at the right.

Power	Action
A-B	Left
A-C	Right
B-C	Center

Figure 3.16 Assembled Flexi in Action
Depending on how it is connected to the batteries, the flexi can be moved in three ways, and bends with a smooth and life-like action.

Figure 3.17 Rubber Figurine with Flexis Inside Its Arms
A rubber figurine with one flexi in each arm. Each hand can move up, down or forward, depending on how it is powered. *Figurine constructed by Judy Brown.*

Depending on which wires are powered, the flexi can bend to the left, right or center (see Figs. 3-15 and 3-16).

How it Works:

The powered wire contracts, and pulls against the tubing. The silicon rubber bends as the wire contracts and also acts as a heat sink to cool the wire when power is removed.

Variations:

• Add eyes to the end of a flexi to make a small "worm".

• Embed several flexis into molded rubber characters or other shapes and give them motion (Fig. 3-17).

PROJECT 6

Ratcheted Rotor & Oscillator Circuit

In this device, a length of Muscle Wire pulls a toothed wheel around step by step. It demonstrates a simple way of transforming linear action into rotation. An electronic oscillator circuit repeatedly activates the wire and has fixed value components for regulating the on time, off time, and current level to the wire.

Rotor Construction:

Assemble the Muscle Wire, crimps, staples and connecting wires, and attach it to the cardboard base as in Project 1. Cut out the cardboard rotor as shown on the pattern sheet (page A-1). Make it using thick cardboard or a plastic sheet, using care to make the teeth as uniform as possible. Cut out and form the two catches (also on the pattern sheet) from card stock.

Make the lever as shown on the pattern sheet using thin cardboard. Attach the lever catch to the lever with tape, and tack the free end of the Muscle Wire at the "W" point. Note that this tack

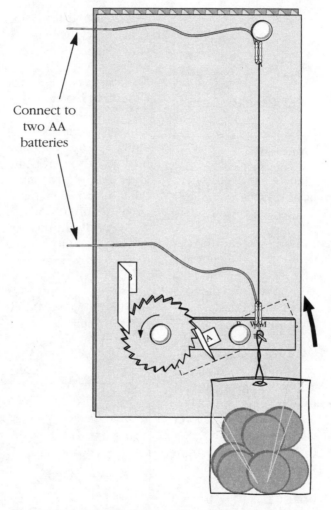

Connect to two AA batteries

Figure 3.18   Project 6, Ratcheted Rotor Mechanism
The device demonstrates a way to convert the linear action of a Muscle Wire into a stepped rotating motion. The angled teeth and the two catches permit the rotor to turn in only one direction.

points outward from the cardboard base. Tack or push pin the lever at the "P" point to the cardboard base. Position the pivot tack to take up all of the slack in the Muscle Wire, and so the lever points to 3 o'clock. Place the coins in the bag and hang from the "W/M" tack on the lever.

		Ratcheted Rotor Parts List
1	each	Muscle Wire, 100 µm dia, 10 cm long
2	each	Crimp (N-scale rail joiner, brass tube, etc.)
2	each	Staple, bent as shown
2	each	Thin connecting wire (#30 wire wrap wire or similar)
4	each	Tack
1	each	Cardboard Base (corrugated)
1	each	Cardboard Lever
1	each	Cardboard Rotor
1	each	Lever Catch (card stock, per pattern)
1	each	Base Catch (card stock, per pattern)
1	each	Small plastic bag
16	each	U.S. 1 cent coins (or other 40 gram mass)
		Tape

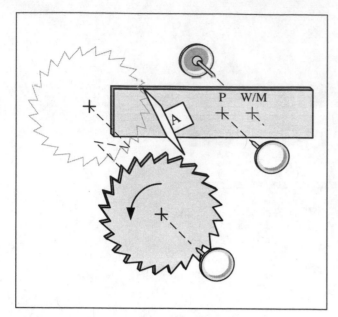

Figure 3.19   Overview of the Rotor Mechanism
Assemble the ratchet parts as shown, noting the direction of the tacks and the rotor's teeth. The left end of the lever arm goes behind the rotor, and helps keep the lever catch in proper position.

It helps to mount the cardboard base vertically in a vice. Tape the connecting wires to the base with enough slack so the lever can move freely.

Tack or push-pin the rotor to the base so that one tooth presses against the lever catch (Fig. 3.18). Note that the lever extends behind the rotor to keep the catch from wandering. Position the base catch on the cardboard base so it also presses against a tooth on the rotor as shown.

Using two AA batteries in the battery holder (the circuit will be tested and added later) briefly apply power to the Muscle Wire. It should contract, pull the lever, and move the catch past at least one tooth on the rotor.

Remove power immediately and let the wire cool. The base catch should let the rotor turn at least one click as the lever relaxes.

If the device needs fine tuning, untape and reposition the base catch, or reposition the fixed end of the Muscle Wire until it works smoothly.

Oscillator Construction:

This circuit can be built using many common methods. Use perf board and soldering for durability, or other methods such as bread board, PCB, etc. Build this circuit and use it to operate this and other projects.

Locate the components on the perf board, and connect them according to the schematic (Fig.

3.21). When assembled, power the circuit with a five volt power supply such as an AC adapter or bench supply.

Test the circuit first on a resistor with the same resistance as the Muscle Wire. Measure the current flow with a meter to insure that it will not over heat the Muscle Wire. Then connect the circuit to the rotor mechanism and watch it rotate.

How it Works:

The powered wire contracts and pulls the lever. The base catch holds the rotor still as the lever moves. When power is removed from the wire, the coins help to extend the Muscle Wire and the lever catch moves the rotor. Together, the two catches let the rotor turn in only one direction.

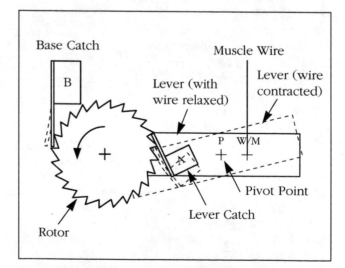

Figure 3.20   Operation of the Rotor Mechanism
The powered wire contracts and pulls the lever. The base catch holds the rotor still as the lever moves. Together, the two catches let the rotor turn in only one direction.

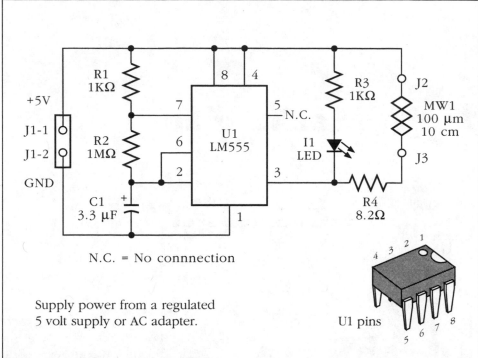

Figure 3.21   Schematic for Project 6, the Oscillator Circuit
Carefully build the circuit as shown. Bread board construction works well for changing the circuit's timing values, and perf board will result in a more durable final circuit. See page 3-3 for more about materials and methods for constructing circuits.

The 555 Integrated Circuit, U1, is a popular "chip" that contains over 40 transistors, resistors and diodes. Here it acts as an oscillator, turning its output (pin 3) on and off according to the values of R1, R2 and C1.

Resistor R3 limits the current to LED I1 to about 5 mA. The LED lights up when Pin 3 of the IC is low and power is flowing through the Muscle Wire. Resistor R4 limits the current to the Muscle Wire to about 160 milliamps (the LM 555 IC can handle up to 200 mA of current).

Changing R1 and R2 varies the ratio of on time to off time, and changing C1 varies the total cycle time. Figure 3.22 shows component values to produce other rates and current levels.

Variations:

• This mechanism can be made very small, flat and lightweight. Use it in animated posters and other limited spaces.

• Build the lever and base using plastic and screws for a longer lasting final product.

• Add more wires and circuitry to create a continuously turning wheel.

TIMING VALUES					
R1	R2	C1	On	Off	Cyc/min
1KΩ	1MΩ	3.3µF	2.5	2.5	12
470KΩ	100KΩ	3.3µF	0.3	1.5	33.3
1KΩ	1MΩ	6.6µF	5	5	6
1MΩ	100KΩ	6.6µF	0.5	5.5	10
470KΩ	100KΩ	10µF	0.7	4.3	12
1MΩ	100KΩ	10µF	0.7	8.3	6.6

CURRENT VALUES				
MW1	R_{mw1}*	R4	W †	i (mA)
50µm	51Ω	35Ω	1/10W	50
50µm	51Ω	0	-	76
100µm	15Ω	12Ω	1/4W	120
100µm	15Ω	9Ω	1/4W	132
100µm	15Ω	0	-	120

* Total resistance of Muscle Wire MW1.
† Minimum wattage of resistor R4.

Figure 3.22   Values to Change the Oscillator Circuit
Different values for R1, R2 and C1 change the oscillation rate and timing, and different values of R4 change the current level through the Muscle Wire MW1.

Latch Mechanism

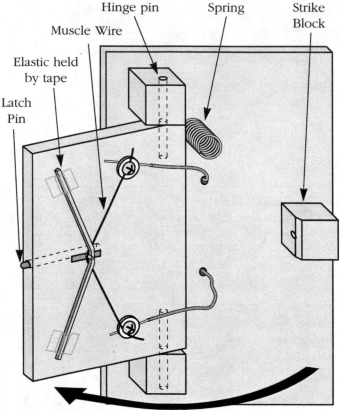

Hinge pin   Spring   Strike Block

Muscle Wire

Elastic held by tape

Latch Pin

Figure 3.23   Project 7, Basic Latch Mechanism
The device shows a way of using a triangular Muscle Wire actuator to release a spring-loaded door. The basic mechanism can be adapted to make an automatic pet feeder, a time lock safe, or a release for concealed panels.

Latch
Parts List

1	each	Muscle Wire, 150 μm dia, 6 cm long
2	each	Screw, flat washers (#2 or #4 size)
2	each	Thin connecting wire (#30 wire wrap wire or similar)
1	each	Latch Pin, brass rod
1	each	Retainer (small nail, wire, etc.)
1	each	Elastic, 8 cm long (or cut rubber band)
2	each	Hinge Pin (small nail, brass rod, etc.)
1	each	Door Panel (plastic, wood, etc.)
1	each	Mounting Base (plastic, wood, etc.)
3	each	Block, strike and hinge (plastic, wood, etc.)
1	each	Compression Spring (from ball point pen or similar)
1	each	Battery, AA size
1	each	Battery Holder, 1 x AA, 1.5 volt
		Glue

In this device, a Muscle Wire retracts a latch pin, permitting a door to spring open. The entire Muscle Wire mechanism mounts on the door itself, and can be extremely thin and lightweight.

Construction:

Make the parts as shown in Figure 3.24. Glue the strike block and hinge blocks to the base (Fig. 3.23). Let the glue dry. Mount the door panel as-

sembly to the hinge blocks with the two hinge pins, making sure the door opens freely and with little slop.

On the inside of the door, add the latch pin, elastic, and Muscle Wire, securing it with screws and flat washers. The latch pin should slide freely in its hole. The elastic must return the pin and Muscle Wire to the extended position, but must not overstrain the Muscle Wire.

Place the compression spring behind the door as shown in Figure 3.23 to push the door open when the latch pin retracts. The spring will put some force on the latch pin when the door is closed, but should not be strong enough to prevent the Muscle Wire from retracting the pin.

Using a single AA battery, briefly apply power to the Muscle Wire. It should contract and retract the latch pin. Remove power immediately and let the wire cool and relax. Close the door manually and power it again. The door should open when the

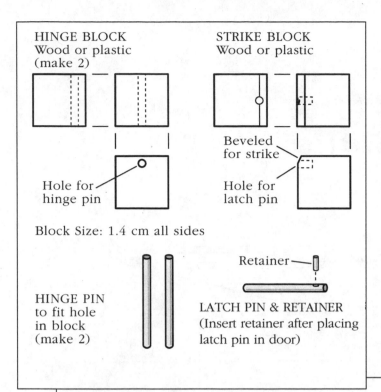

HINGE BLOCK
Wood or plastic
(make 2)

Hole for
hinge pin

STRIKE BLOCK
Wood or plastic

Beveled
for strike

Hole for
latch pin

Block Size: 1.4 cm all sides

HINGE PIN
to fit hole
in block
(make 2)

Retainer

LATCH PIN & RETAINER
(Insert retainer after placing
latch pin in door)

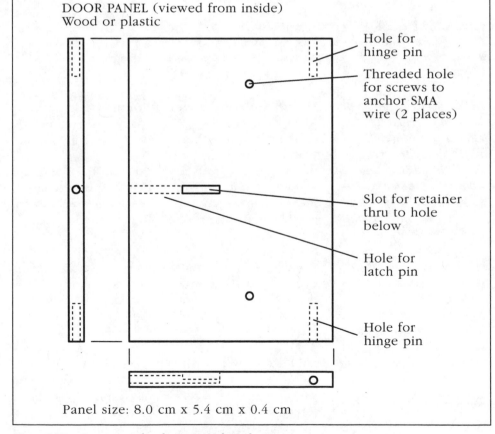

DOOR PANEL (viewed from inside)
Wood or plastic

Hole for
hinge pin

Threaded hole
for screws to
anchor SMA
wire (2 places)

Slot for retainer
thru to hole
below

Hole for
latch pin

Hole for
hinge pin

Panel size: 8.0 cm x 5.4 cm x 0.4 cm

Figure 3.24 Components for the Basic Latch Mechanism
Make these parts from plastic or wood. Many variations are possible, so
adjust the parts to match the materials you have available.

latch pin retracts. If the device needs fine tuning, adjust the screws holding the Muscle Wire until the pin retracts enough to release the door.

How it Works:

When powered, the Wire contracts and retracts the latch pin, pulling against the elastic. The retracting pin reaches a point where it no longer holds the door panel closed, and the force of the compression spring pushes the door open.

When power is removed, the force of the elastic band extends the Muscle Wire and pushes the latch pin back out. When the door is pushed closed, the latch pin catches on the strike plate and holds the door closed.

Variations:

• Use this device for unlocking concealed panels, covering secret hiding places, releasing guards on protected switches, etc.

• Add an electronic driver circuit (as in Project 6) for continuous operation. It can be built compactly and mounted on the latch mechanism.

• Use a time delay circuit (as in Project 11) to unlock or release a latch at a preset time. This can make a great automatic pet feeder, a time lock safe, or an electronic "surprise package".

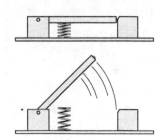

Figure 3.25 Latch in Action
The Muscle Wire retracts the latch pin and frees the spring to push open the door panel.

Reverse Bias Marble Roller

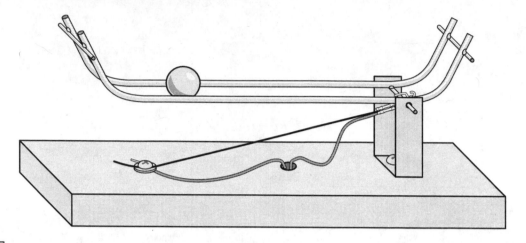

Figure 3.26   Project 8, Reverse Bias Marble Roller
As the Muscle Wire lifts the channel, the marble rolls and reduces the force on the wire. With power removed, the wire relaxes, lowering the channel, and the marble rolls back.

Marble Roller
Parts List

1	each	Muscle Wire, 100 µ m dia, 8 cm long
1	each	Crimp (N-scale rail joiner, brass tube, etc.)
1	each	Staple, bent as shown
2	each	Thin connecting wire (#30 wire wrap wire or similar)
1	each	Base (wood, plastic, metal, etc.)
2	each	Brass Tube, 3 mm dia, 15 cm long (for rails)
2	each	Brass Rod, 1.5 mm dia, 2 cm long (cross bars)
1	each	Brass Wire, 1.5 cm long (for loop)
1	each	Brass Sheet (for stand)
1	each	Marble, approx. 14 mm dia
1	each	Screw, nut, flat washer
		Solder and flux for brass

In this device, a length of Muscle Wire lifts a curved channel, rolling a marble. As the marble moves it lowers the force applied to the contracting Muscle Wire, and produces a reverse bias effect (see page 2-12).

When connected to the oscillator circuit from Project 6, this project can run continuously, and makes an excellent demonstration of the abilities of Muscle Wires.

Construction:

Assemble the Muscle Wire, crimp, staple and the connecting wire as shown in Figure 3.27.

Make the parts for the roller channel as shown on the pattern sheet (page A-2). Bend the two brass tube side rails as shown, using care to make them as smooth and identical as possible.

Solder the cross bars in place, spacing the rails evenly so that the marble, when placed in the channel, does not touch the cross bars.

Solder the loop to the channel. It should be smoothly bent, and centered in the channel. Drill and form the stand as shown. Cut and drill the base from a block of wood or plastic.

You may add a hollow space to contain the drive circuit if you wish.

Position the stand, add the completed channel, attach the Muscle Wire to the loop, and catch the free end of Muscle Wire under the screw. Adjust the wire so the channel points slightly below horizontal. Finally, place the marble on the channel and test it.

Using two AA batteries in the battery holder (or an electronic driver circuit) briefly apply power to the Muscle Wire. It should contract and lift the channel above horizontal, rolling the mar-

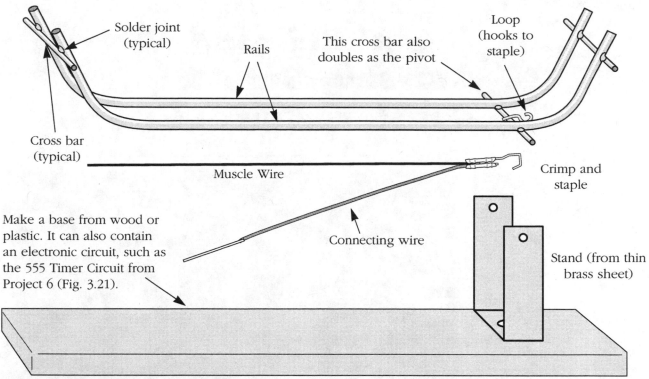

Figure 3.27 Parts for the Reverse Bias Marble Roller
Build and assemble these parts as shown. The screw and washer catch and hold the Muscle Wire, and provide an adjustable connection. The brass rails must be spaced evenly to make a smooth track for the marble.

ble. Remove power and let the wire cool and relax. If the device needs fine tuning, adjust the end of the wire held by the screw until the marble rolls smoothly.

How it Works:

The powered wire contracts and lifts the channel, raising the marble and causing it to roll. As the marble moves towards the pivot point, it reduces the force on the Muscle Wire, providing a reverse bias effect and greatly extending the wire's life.

When power is removed the weight of the channel helps extend the wire.

When the channel drops below horizontal the marble rolls back (Fig. 3.28).

If properly constructed this roller can operate continuously for years. Six cycles per minute will yield over 3.15 million cycles per year – an impressive demonstration of Muscle Wire life.

Variations:

• Add an electronic driver circuit (as in Project 6) for continuous operation. It can be built compactly and mounted inside the base. Power it with an AC adapter for a continuously running demonstration project.

• Another version of this device uses a low force lever switch mounted in the channel opposite the pivot. The marble (or a heavier ball bearing for more force) presses on the switch and it runs without any electronics.

• Use a transparent "crackled" marble and place the roller in a sunny window. It will shine and reflect light all around the room.

Thanks to Jeff Brown for the marble roller design.

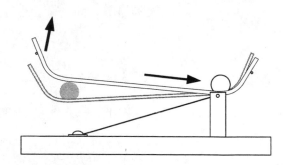

Figure 3.28 The Marble Roller in Action
As the Muscle Wire contracts, it lifts the channel and the marble rolls, reducing the bias force on the wire.

Model Railroad Crossing Gate & Constant Current Circuit

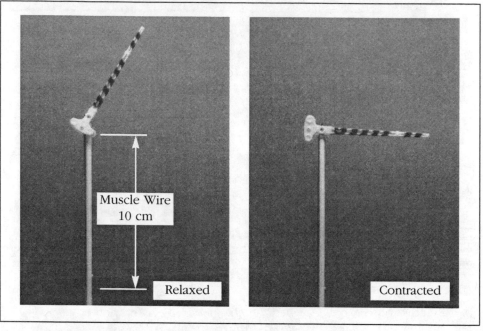

Muscle Wire
10 cm

Relaxed

Contracted

Figure 3.29   Project 9, Model Railroad Crossing Gate in Action
On the left, the Muscle Wire in the crossing gate is unpowered and relaxed. On the right, the wire is powered and pulls the gate down. This device demonstrates how Muscle Wires can create animation in model railroads, dioramas, doll houses, and other miniature settings.

In this device, a Muscle Wire lowers a crossing gate for an HO-scale model train. The 12 volt DC driver circuit regulates the power to the Muscle Wire using a voltage regulator to provide a constant level of current.

The circuit can be connected to other parts of standard railroad control systems, and made to operate as a train passes.

Crossing Gate Construction:

You may use a commercially available model crossing gate or build your own. The example shown uses an arm from Bachmann Industries' "Crossing Signals and Gates" (#42200) available from hobby and model train retailers. The arm is modified as shown in Figure 3.30.

Crimp the Muscle Wire and the thin connecting wire together, and tie a 3 cm length of flexible but non-stretching cord (like nylon *squidding line*, available where fishing supplies are sold) to the crimp. Tie a loop in the other end of the flexible cord, and attach the loop to the gate arm with the small pin, making sure the gate arm moves freely (Fig. 3.31).

The flexible cord acts as a tendon, extending the force of the Muscle Wire, and passing over a bend with a radius too small for the Muscle Wire.

Tie the elastic in a loop and position it over the anchor pin on the crossing gate arm. Secure the Muscle Wire and elastic to the main support tube with the staples formed as shown in Figure 3.30. Adjust the elastic so it pulls the gate arm to the upright position, and so there is no slack in the Muscle Wire.

Protect the Muscle Wire from damage by placing the lower end of the mechanism inside a tube. To mount it on a railroad layout, drill a hole and insert the tube until the arm is at the correct height.

Using two AA batteries in the battery holder, briefly apply power to the Muscle Wire. It should contract and pull the crossing arm down.

Figure 3.31   Gate Operation
When the Muscle Wire contracts, it pulls the gate arm down. With power removed, the wire relaxes and the elastic pulls the gate arm back up. Note how the position of the elastic's anchor pin helps create a reverse bias where the elastic stretches less as the gate arm lowers past a certain point.

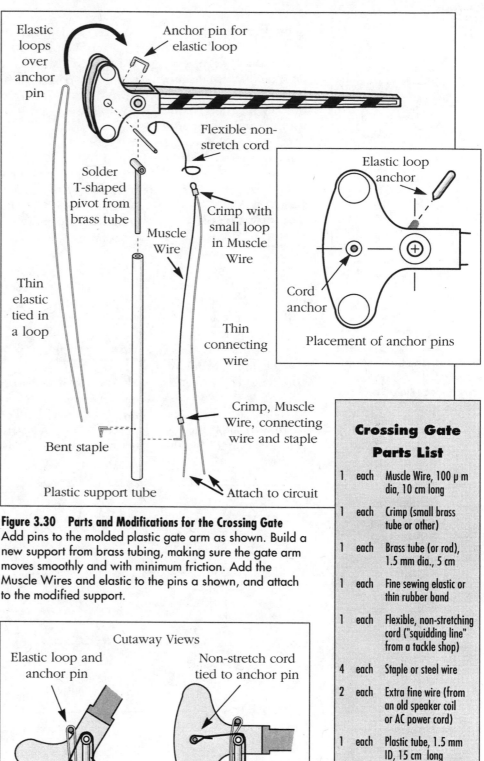

Figure 3.30   Parts and Modifications for the Crossing Gate
Add pins to the molded plastic gate arm as shown. Build a new support from brass tubing, making sure the gate arm moves smoothly and with minimum friction. Add the Muscle Wires and elastic to the pins a shown, and attach to the modified support.

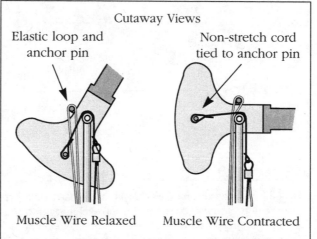

Cutaway Views

Muscle Wire Relaxed   Muscle Wire Contracted

Crossing Gate Parts List

1	each	Muscle Wire, 100 µ m dia, 10 cm long
1	each	Crimp (small brass tube or other)
1	each	Brass tube (or rod), 1.5 mm dia., 5 cm
1	each	Fine sewing elastic or thin rubber band
1	each	Flexible, non-stretching cord ("squidding line" from a tackle shop)
4	each	Staple or steel wire
2	each	Extra fine wire (from an old speaker coil or AC power cord)
1	each	Plastic tube, 1.5 mm ID, 15 cm long
1	each	HO-scale RR Crossing Gate (see text)
		Solder for brass
		Glue

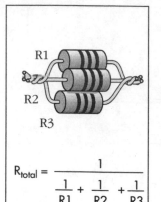

$$R_{total} = \cfrac{1}{\cfrac{1}{R1} + \cfrac{1}{R2} + \cfrac{1}{R3}}$$

If resistors have same resistance & wattage then:

$$W_{total} = W_{R1} + W_{R2} + W_{R3}$$

Figure 3.32   Power Resistor Resistors can be combined in parallel for a smaller resistance (Rtotal) and larger wattages (Wtotal), using these equations.

Remove power immediately and let the wire cool and relax. The elastic should return the arm to its upright position. If the device needs fine tuning, reposition the fixed end of the Muscle Wire, or adjust the elastic band.

Constant Current Circuit Construction:

This circuit can be built using many common methods. Use perf board and soldering for durability. Locate the components on the perf board, and connect them according to the schematic (Fig. 3.33).

Resistor R1 limits the current produced by the voltage regulator. It can be made with two 10 Ω 1/4 watt resistors connected in parallel (Fig 3.32). For other current levels see the table in Figure 3.34

When fully assembled, first test the circuit on a separate length of Muscle Wire, then attach it to the connecting wires of the crossing gate and watch it move the arm. Use a 12 volt power supply or AC adapter, using care to properly connect the (+) and (-) sides.

How it Works:

The powered wire contracts and pulls the crossing gate down. When power is removed the elastic helps extend the wire and returns the arm to the upright position.

The 317T integrated circuit is a power regulator containing over 50 transistors, resistors, capacitors and diodes. Here it acts as a current limiter to control the power to the Muscle Wire. It can handle up to 1.5 amps, depending on the capacity of the power supply.

The current produced by the regulator is determined by: 1.25 ÷ R, where R is the resistance in ohms of R1. When switch SW1 closes, power flows through resistor R2 to the base of transistor Q1. Power then flows between the emitter and collector of Q1 and through the Muscle Wire.

Constant Current Circuit Parts List

1	U1	IC, 317T Regulator (Jameco #23579)
1	R1	Res, 5Ω, 1/2 watt (use two 10Ω, 1/4W resistor in parallel. See text and Fig 3.32)
1	R2	Res, 100K Ω, 1/4 watt (Brn, Blk, Yel, Gold)
1	R3	Res, 39K Ω, 1/4 watt (Org, Wht, Org, Gold)
1	Q1	Trans, MPS A13 NPN, Darl. Amp. (Jameco #26489)
1	SW1	Switch, normally open
1	U1	Heat sink, TO-220 style
		Hook-up Wire
		Perf board

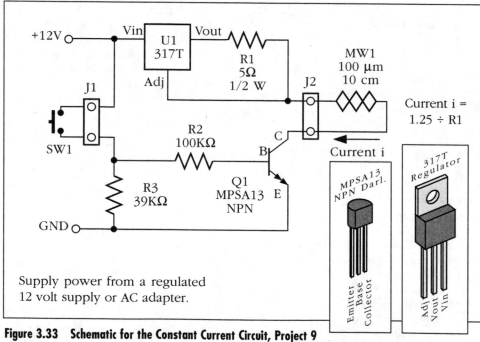

Supply power from a regulated 12 volt supply or AC adapter.

Figure 3.33   Schematic for the Constant Current Circuit, Project 9
This circuit provides a constant current level through a Muscle Wire , regardless of its length. The circuit can be modified for other sizes of Muscle Wire, other current levels, and other input voltages. See Figure 3.34 for other component values.

Resistor R3 provides a small bias voltage to the base of Q1 to help turn it off and stop the current when switch SW1 opens.

This is a good circuit for a single size of Muscle Wire under consistent conditions (like room temperature in still air). If the limit is correctly chosen for the surrounding conditions, the circuit will protect the wire from overheating *regardless of its length,* up to the maximum voltage of the power supply and regulator.

However, this circuit is less efficient for shorter lengths of Muscle Wire, as it must burn off any power that the wire does not use. The most efficient power usage comes when operating wires at or near the maximum length for the circuit. See Figure 3.34.

Variations:

• For repeated operation (such as for testing or demonstration purposes) connect to an automatic timing circuit as in projects 6 and 14.

• For additional action connect this gate to the circuit in Figure 3.35 that will flash crossing lights as well as lower two crossing gates.

• *Model Railroader* magazine, March 1993, page 100, has another Muscle Wire gate mechanism for use with Figure 3.35.

RESISTOR VALUES FOR VARIOUS MUSCLE WIRE SIZES

MW1	R_{MW1}*	Vin**	Vout	R1	W_{R1} †	i (mA)
50	51	6.0	3.8	25	0.06	50
50	51	6.0	4.4	20	0.08	62
50	51	8.0	6.6	12	0.13	104
100	15	6.0	4.0	7	0.23	180
100	15	7.0	5.0	5	0.31	250
100	15	9.0	6.8	3.3	0.46	370
150	5	5.0	3.3	3	0.50	400
150	5	6.0	3.9	2.5	0.65	520
150	5	7.0	5.3	1.5	1.00	800
250	2	5.0	3.3	1.25	1.25	1000
250	2	6.0	3.9	1	1.63	1300
250	2	6.0	4.3	0.8	1.88	1500

* Total resistance of Muscle Wire MW1.
** Minimum input voltage – can be higher (e.g. 12 or 24 V)
† Minimum wattage of resistor R1.

Figure 3.34   Values for Other Wire Sizes and Current Levels
For current levels to power other sizes of Muscle Wire, use the voltages and resistors shown in place of the components given in Figure 3.33 and 3.35.

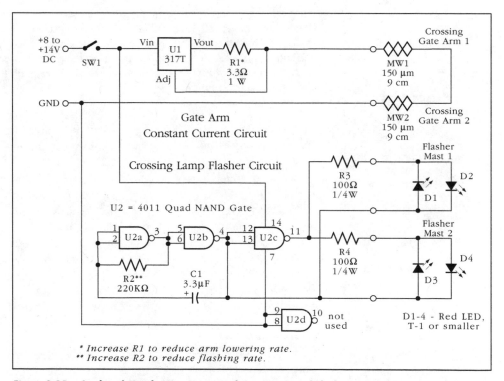

Figure 3.35   Combined Muscle Wire Driver and Crossing Signal Flasher Circuit for Two Gates
Switch SW1 closes and powers Muscle Wires MW1 and 2, and the circuit which alternates flashes the red LEDs (D1-4). See Figure 3.46 for more on the 4011 integrated circuit (U2).

Lamp Flasher & AC Power Circuit

WARNING: This circuit uses AC power and voltages that can be DANGEROUS OR FATAL. Use proper precautions when setting up and testing this device.

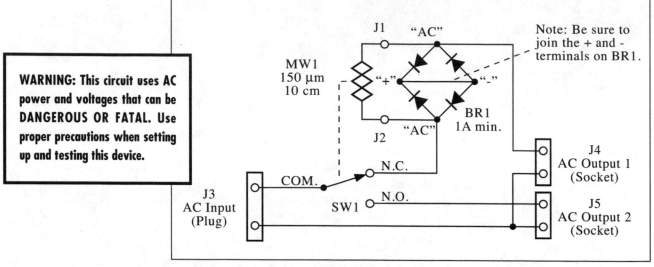

Figure 3.36   Project 10, Lamp Flasher & AC Power Circuit
The device uses the small voltage drop that occurs across a diode to power a Muscle Wire and toggle a switch to flash an AC powered lamp. Each diode provides a 0.7 volt drop, for a combined 1.4 volt drop across the Muscle Wire, with two diodes acting during each part of the AC current cycle.

Parts List

1	A1	Muscle Wire, 150 µ m dia, 10 cm long
1	SW1	SPDT switch, contacts rated 110 VAC, 1 A minimum (see text)
2	J1-2	Screw, nut, flat washer (#2 or #4 size)
1	BR1	Bridge Rectifier, 110 VAC, 1.5 Amp (Jameco #145429)
1	J3	AC Power Cord (see text)
2	J4-5	AC Outlet (see text)
		Perf board
		Enclosure
		Hookup wire

In this device, a Muscle Wire contracts to toggle a switch and turn off its own power. With power removed the wire relaxes until the switch turns on again and the cycle repeats. This simple oscillator takes power directly from the AC line, and can be used to flash a desk lamp, chains of lights, etc.

Construction:

This combined circuit and Muscle Wire mechanism can be built using many common methods. Use perf board and soldering for durability, or mount on a PCB.

The switch must be a single pole double throw type with normally closed (N.C.) and normally open (N.O.) contacts, and be rated for 110 VAC at 1 amp or more. Failure to use a properly rated switch can be dangerous.

The cord and outlets can be standard electrical parts, available at hardware stores. Position the components on the perf board as shown in Figure 3.37 and connect them as shown.

Secure the Muscle Wire with screws, and adjust so it just begins to pull the switch down. Be sure that the wire is loose enough so that the switch, when depressed, can rise and turn on again.

For safety, insulate all exposed AC power connections and mount the entire project inside an insulated enclosure.

Testing:

This device works only with a load connected at socket J4, as AC power must be flowing through the circuit to power the Muscle Wire. When testing the circuit use a lamp of 40 watts or more and be prepared to quickly remove power, as overheating can damage the Muscle Wire.

If the device does not oscillate, unplug it, check all connections and adjust the Muscle Wire. If it is too loose, it will not depress the switch even when fully contracted. If too tight, it will not relax enough to release the switch again.

The switch must exert enough force to return the cooled wire to its starting position, but not so much as to prevent the contracting wire from moving it. The switch must also have a small enough hysteresis so the wire can turn it on and off (see page 1-2 for more about hysteresis).

If even with careful adjusting the device will not function, you may need to use a switch that has a weaker internal spring or a longer lever arm.

How it Works:

Power to heat the Muscle Wire comes from the 0.7 volt drop that occurs across a diode. The four diodes in rectifier BR1

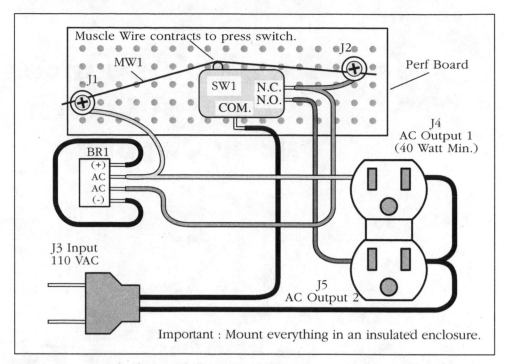

Figure 3.37 Layout for the Lamp Flasher & AC Power Circuit
Construct this device carefully and use caution when testing. Rectifier BR1, wired in to the main flow of AC current, creates a small voltage drop that heats the Muscle Wire and causes it to contract.

are connected so that AC current flows through them (in either direction as the current alternates) and produces a 1.4 volt drop across MW1.

Current flows through the Muscle Wire and heats it. As it contracts it depresses the switch and turns off the power to the wire and the external load at socket J4, and turns on power to the normally open contacts and the socket J5. As the wire cools and elongates, the switch flips again and the cycle repeats.

The hysteresis of the switch and the cooling conditions around the wire influence the rate of oscillation.

Variations:

• Try blowing on the Muscle Wire while it is operating. How does it affect the speed and timing of the oscillator?

• Build a device with just a switch and two AA batteries (no rectifier or AC) to make a battery powered oscillator.

• Make a low power relay with a switch rated for 110 VAC and a Muscle Wire that can be powered with 1.5 volts. Almost all solenoid-driven relays require 5 volts or more. With Muscle Wires you can make relays using very low voltages, and require very little space.

Thanks to Dr. Dai Homma for the design of this oscillator project.

Airplane Launcher & Digital Watch Timer Circuit

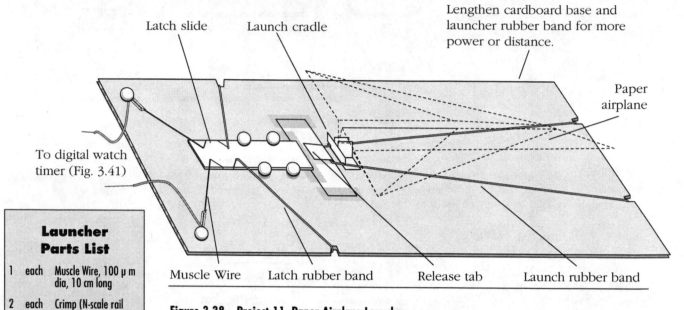

Latch slide   Launch cradle

Lengthen cardboard base and launcher rubber band for more power or distance.

Paper airplane

To digital watch timer (Fig. 3.41)

Muscle Wire   Latch rubber band   Release tab   Launch rubber band

Figure 3.38   Project 11, Paper Airplane Launcher
This project uses a digital watch to activate a Muscle Wire, which releases a rubber band to launch a paper airplane from this simple launcher. This circuit and mechanism can be the basis for a timed pet feeder, a release for a kite-borne parachute, or many similar devices.

Launcher Parts List

1	each	Muscle Wire, 100 μm dia, 10 cm long
2	each	Crimp (N-scale rail joiner, or other)
2	each	Staple, bent as shown
2	each	Thin connecting wire (#30 wire wrap wire or similar)
6	each	Tack or push pin
1	each	Cardboard base (corrugated)
1	each	Thin cardboard
1	each	Mylar, 0.15 mm thick (or acetate, etc.)
1	each	Long rubber band, for launcher
1	each	Short rubber band, for latch bias force
1	each	Small paper airplane (from half-size sheet)
		Tape
		Glue

In this device, a Muscle Wire releases a latch holding a stretched rubber band ready to launch a paper airplane. The circuit uses an inexpensive digital watch with an alarm to activate the Muscle Wire and launch the plane at a preset time.

Construction:

Assemble the Muscle Wire, crimps, staples and connecting wires as in Project 1, and mount to the cardboard base in a triangular arrangement as shown in Figure 3.39.

Attach the short rubber band to provide a bias force to the Muscle Wire. Cut out and form the latch slide and release tab as shown on the pattern sheets (page A-2). Tape the release tab securely to the base cardboard as shown. Position and hold the cardboard slide with tacks on both sides, and pass the rubber band and Muscle Wire through the notches on the slide as shown in Figure 3.39. The slide should move freely, and catch the folded release tab by just two or three millimeters.

Cut out and glue together the launch cradle as shown on page A-2 and Figure 3.39. Attach it to the long rubber band, and attach the rubber band to

           Roger G. Gilbertson

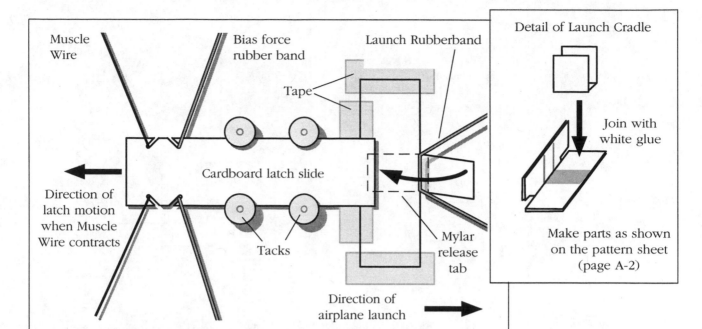

Figure 3.39 Detail of Latch and Launch Cradle
When powered, the Muscle Wire contracts and pulls back on the slide, which frees the tab holding the launcher rubber band. The force of the rubber band pulls the tab open, and when free, launches the plane.

the base. Stretch the long rubber band over the release tab as shown in Figure 3.39. It should exert enough force to launch the paper airplane, but not so much as to damage the release tab when latched.

Using the battery pack, briefly apply power to the Muscle Wire. It should contract and pull the slide away from the release tab, which will open and release the long rubber band, launching the airplane. Remove power immediately and let the wire cool and relax.

Constructing the Digital Watch Timer Circuit:

This circuit can be built using many common

methods. Use perf board and soldering for durability. Locate the components on the perf board, and connect them according to the schematic (Fig. 3.41).

The digital watch can be any common and inexpensive type (showroom and discount department stores are likely places to find them), but it must have an alarm.

Carefully open the back of the digital watch. To connect it to the driver circuit locate and solder wires to two points: 1) the positive voltage side of the battery, and 2) the alarm output point.

Most watches run on either 1.5 or 3 volts. With a volt meter, find a posi-

tive voltage point on the circuit board at or near the battery (or batteries). Use a thin hookup wire and just enough solder to attach to the positive voltage point (not directly to the battery).

The alarm buzzer should be a thin dull gold or silver disk inside the back cover. On the watch circuit, look for a small spring or metal finger that touches the buzzer when the cover is in place. This is the alarm output. Solder another thin hookup wire to the output point.

Cut or file a notch in the back cover and replace it, passing the two wires through the notch. With a volt meter, recheck the connections at the ends

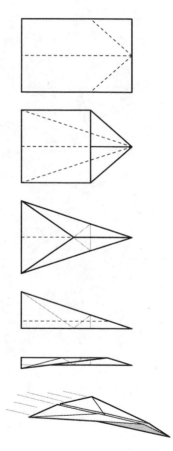

Figure 3.40 Basic Airplane
Follow these steps to make a paper airplane, or use a small paper or balsa wood glider.

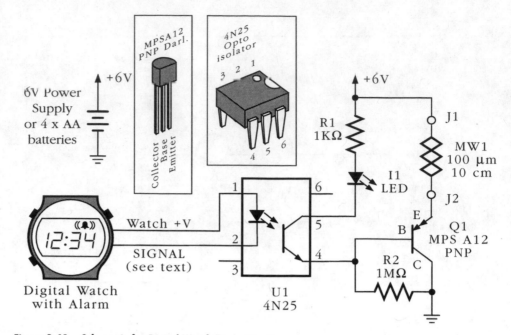

Figure 3.41   Schematic for Digital Watch Timer Circuit
This circuit connects the alarm output of a standard digital watch to an optoisolator (U1).
When the alarm activates, it applies power to the Muscle Wire, and launches the plane.

of the hookup wires. With the alarm active you should see a varying signal, from 0 to 1.5 or 3 V, depending on the watch.

Finally, connect the wires from the watch to the circuit in Figure 3.41. Test the alarm to be sure that the red LED lights when it triggers. Finally, attach the circuit to the assembled airplane launcher, and test the entire system.

How It Works:

When powered, the Muscle Wire pulls the latch slide, freeing the release tab and letting the rubber band launch the plane. When power is removed the small rubber band helps extend the Muscle Wire and the launcher can be reset. The digital watch con-

tains very sophisticated electronics in a small, inexpensive package. The oscillating signal that normally powers the watch's buzzer provides a low signal to Pin 2 of U1, the optoisolator.

Inside U1, the signal lights an LED which shines on a photo transistor and permits power to flow from Pin 5 to Pin 4. This lights the red LED I1, and provides a positive voltage to the base of Q1. With the base positive, power flows between its emitter and collector and through the Muscle Wire. If you listen closely, you may be able to hear the wire oscillating with the sound of the watch's buzzer.

Resistor R1 limits the current to LED I1, and R2 provides a bias to pull

the base of Q1 to low and fully turn it off.

Variations:

• Place the launcher on a book shelf or other hidden place and set the timer for a time when someone is likely to be present.

• Attach the timer circuit to a kite and make a device to drop a parachute or glider at a preset time from high in the air.

• Use the circuit to unlock or release a latch at a preset time for an automatic pet feeder, a time lock "safe", or an automatic "surprise".

• Use this circuit to activate other driver circuits, such as the constant current circuit in Project 10.

PROJECT 12

Life-like Butterfly & PWM Circuit

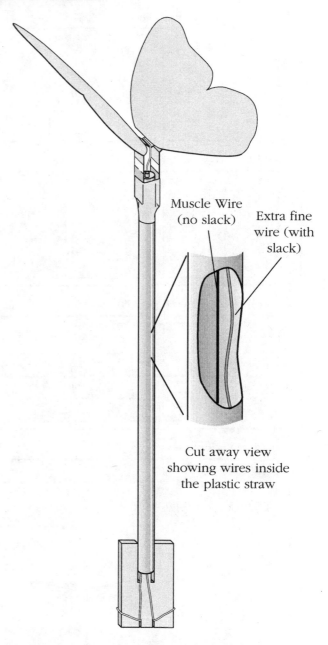

Muscle Wire
(no slack)

Extra fine
wire (with
slack)

Cut away view
showing wires inside
the plastic straw

Figure 3.42   Project 12, Butterfly Mechanism
The thin party straw houses the Muscle Wire and holds the special wing base strip. When the wire contracts it closes the wing base to simulate the motion of a living butterfly.

Lifelike Butterfly Parts List

1	each	Muscle Wire, 100 µ m dia, 10 cm long (or 50 µ m with light wings)
1	each	Straw, 3 mm dia. 12 cm long (party or cocktail type)
1	each	Crimp (small brass tube or similar)
2	each	Staple, bent as shown
2	each	Thin connecting wire (#30 wire wrap wire or similar)
1	each	Extra fine wire (from an old speaker or microphone coil)
1	each	Cardboard base (corrugated)
2	each	Paper wing (see text)
1	each	Mylar or Acetate sheet, 150 µ m thick (0.006 inch)
		Tape, transparent
		Tape, double sided

In this device, a length of Muscle Wire lifts a pair of light weight butterfly wings (paper or real), with a smooth, life-like motion. The pulse width modulation (PWM) circuit turns the power to the wire rapidly on and off, and uses battery power very efficiently.

Construction:

Make the wingbase by cutting carefully spaced slots in the mylar sheet (Fig. 3.43-A) with a sharp hobby knife, then taping over them (3.43-B) with clear tape. Next add four strips of double-sided tape (3.43-C), and then cut the sheet crosswise (3.43-D) to form two or more wingbase strips. By using larger sheets of mylar, you can form as many strips as needed.

Assemble the Muscle Wire, crimps, bent staple and connecting wires as shown in Figure 3.44.

A) Cut seven slots, spaced as shown, in 0.15 mm thick mylar sheet.

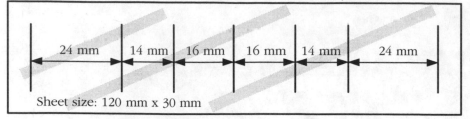

24 mm   14 mm   16 mm   16 mm   14 mm   24 mm

Sheet size: 120 mm x 30 mm

B) Cover slots with five pieces of clear, flexible adhesive tape (top side only).

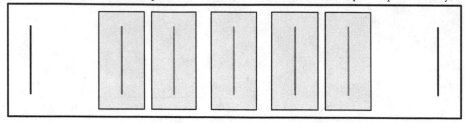

C) Add four strips of double-sided clear tape (and protect with wax paper).

(on bottom side)   (on top side)   (on top side)   (on bottom side)

D) Cut three horizontal slots, spaced 6 mm apart, to make two strips.

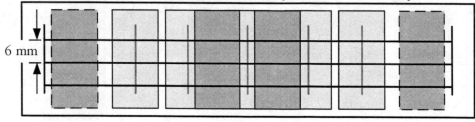

6 mm

E) Final wingbase strip.

F) Wingbase strip folded (double-sided tapes in center face upwards).

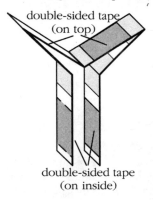

double-sided tape
(on top)

double-sided tape
(on inside)

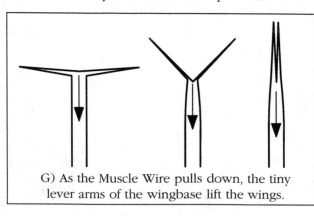

G) As the Muscle Wire pulls down, the tiny lever arms of the wingbase lift the wings.

Attach the wingbase strip to the top of the straw, and secure it with tape. Be sure the strip is mounted evenly on the straw, and that it closes pointing straight away from the straw (Fig. 3.43-G). Insert the cardboard base into the other end of the straw.

Thread the Muscle Wire assembly through the straw, and hook the staple over the center of the wingbase. Pass the wires on either side of the cardboard base and pass them through the slots to hold them. Leave slack in the insulated connecting wire, and tighten the Muscle Wire so the wingbase just begins to close (adjust as shown in Figure 3.45).

Attach the paper butterfly wings to the wingbase tabs using small pieces of double sided tape.

Briefly apply battery power to the Muscle Wire. It should contract and pull the wingbase tabs fully closed. Remove power immediately and let the wire cool and relax. The wing base should open

Figure 3.43 Making the Wingbase Strip
The thin plastic and tape structure makes a dual lever that amplifies the small action of the Muscle Wire, and creates a large sweeping wing motion.

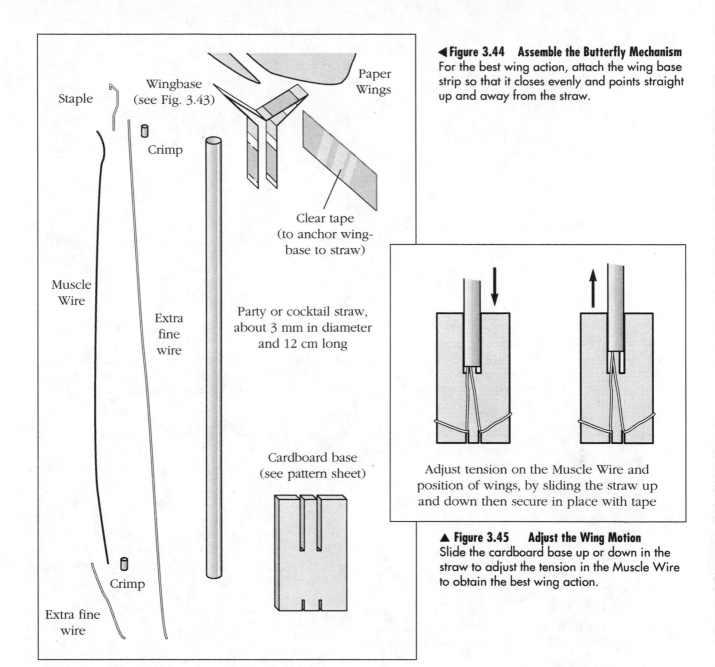

◄ Figure 3.44   Assemble the Butterfly Mechanism
For the best wing action, attach the wing base strip so that it closes evenly and points straight up and away from the straw.

Staple

Wingbase
(see Fig. 3.43)

Paper
Wings

Crimp

Clear tape
(to anchor wing-
base to straw)

Muscle
Wire

Extra
fine
wire

Party or cocktail straw,
about 3 mm in diameter
and 12 cm long

Cardboard base
(see pattern sheet)

Crimp

Extra fine
wire

Adjust tension on the Muscle Wire and
position of wings, by sliding the straw up
and down then secure in place with tape

▲ Figure 3.45   Adjust the Wing Motion
Slide the cardboard base up or down in the straw to adjust the tension in the Muscle Wire to obtain the best wing action.

again, assisted by the weight of the wings.

Constructing the Pulse Width Modulation Circuit:

This circuit can be built using many common methods. Use perf board and soldering for durability. Locate the compo-nents on the perf board, and connect them ac-cording to the schematic in Figure 3.46.

Connect the circuit to the butterfly mechanism and watch it run. Remember, if the wire does not begin to relax upon removal of power, then too much heat is being generated, and the input voltage or duty ratio should be reduced.

How it Works:

When powered, the Muscle Wire pulls down on the center of the wing-base, and lifts the wings up. When power is re-moved, the weight of the

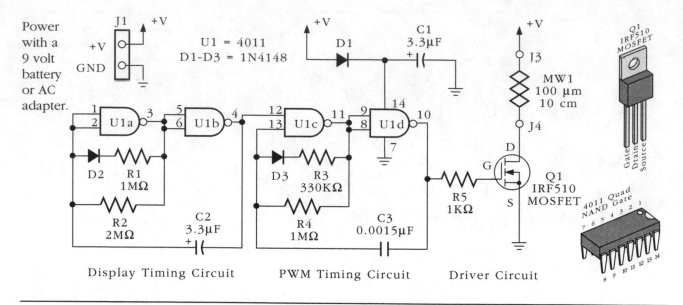

Power with a 9 volt battery or AC adapter.

U1 = 4011
D1–D3 = 1N4148

Display Timing Circuit | PWM Timing Circuit | Driver Circuit

Figure 3.46 Schematic for Pulse Width Modulation Circuit

This circuit drives a Muscle Wire without using a current limiting resistor. The display timing section produces the on and off signal that controls the rate that the wings open and close. The PWM timing section controls the fast on and off cycle (active only when the wings are to move up) that regulates the heating of the Muscle Wire.

PWM Circuit Parts List

1	U1	IC, 4011 Quad NAND gate (Jameco #12634)
2	R1,4	Res, 1M Ω, 1/4 W (Brn, Blk, Grn, Gold)
1	R2	Res, 2M Ω, 1/4 W (Red, Blk, Grn, Gold)
1	R3	Res, 330K Ω, 1/4 W (Org, Org, Yel, Gold)
1	R5	Res, 1K Ω, 1/4 W (Brn, Blk, Red, Gold)
3	D1-3	Diode, 1N4148 small signal
2	C1,2	Cap, 3.3 μ F, 16 V min. alum. electrolytic
1	C3	Cap, 0.0015 μ F
1	Q1	IRF510, N-channel Power MOSFET (Jameco #209234)
1	U1	Socket, 14 pin, DIP
1	J1	Connector, 9V snap
		Perf board
		Hookup wire

wings helps extend the Muscle Wire and reopen the wings.

The 4011 Integrated Circuit uses very little power, and is wired to form a dual oscillator. When the first stage of the 4011 oscillator (U1-a and b) are active, then the second stage (U1-c and d) can operate to drive the Muscle Wire.

The first part of the circuit controls the display timing which sets the up and down rate of the wings. The rate and duty ratio are determined by components R1, R2, D2 and C1.

The second stage controls the PWM duty ratio and regulates the amount of power and heat generated in the Muscle

Wire. It is controlled by R3, R4, D3 and C3.

Resistor R5 regulates the PWM signal to the base of the MOSFET (Metal Oxide Semiconductor Field Effect Transistor) Q1, which controls the actual power output to

the Muscle Wire. Figure 3.47 shows the timing of the PWM output signal.

This driver circuit works especially well for small, self contained, repeatedly activated devices in display, demonstration, or for long term testing pur-

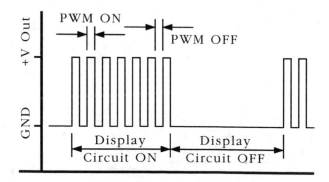

Figure 3.47 Typical PWM Output

Typical output of the PWM driver circuit. Each ON cycle consists of a modulated signal to activate the Muscle Wire. Different values produce other timing and power levels.

Roger G. Gilbertson

poses. A 9 volt alkaline-type battery can run this circuit for over 10 hours of continuous operation.

Variations:

• For a more realistic butterfly, use photographs of real butterfly wings or hand colored wings, add a fuzzy body with thin wires for legs and antennae, and beads for eyes.

• Mount the butterfly in a silk flower arrangement and replace the battery with an DC adapter for a continuous display.

• For a faster moving butterfly, use 50 μm diameter Muscle Wire, and very light wings. Adjust the

PWM timing section of the circuit for the smaller wire, and the display timing section for the faster motion. The thinner wire can be driven at 10 cycles per minute or more, as it cools faster than the larger diameter wires.

• For a sun powered device, build the circuit in Figure 3.49 below. It uses solar cells to power the Muscle Wire and charge a set of NiCad batteries.

To use a solar array that provides less than 9 volts, slow down the display timing circuit (change R1 and/or R2) or use a smaller diameter Muscle Wire which will require less power.

Figure 3.48   Semi-realistic Animated Butterfly
The body is a pipe cleaner, antennas and legs are thin wires, and the tiny eyes are gold beads. The wings are color photocopies of real wings glued back-to-back. When placed with real or silk flowers, the moving butterfly adds a captivating, life-like accent.

Sun Powered SMAs

Use this basic circuit to run the butterfly and PWM circuit (Fig.3.46). You can adapt it to work with most any solar cells or panels. Simply wire the cells in series (+ to -) to obtain the required voltage (around 9 volts).

Typically, NiCad batteries produce 1.2 volts per cell, so the 9 volt circuit will need 7 or 8 cells, also wired in series (Fig. 3.49).

Note that solar cells produce a constant *voltage,* and that the current produced varies with the amount of light striking their surface. This means the PWM circuit will con-

tinue running until there is too little current to drive the wire, and in bright

light, any excess current will charge the NiCads for later use.

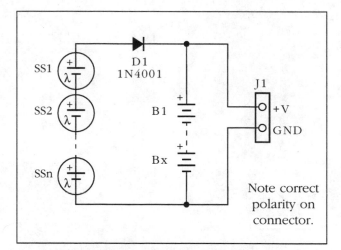

Figure 3.49   Solar Power Source & Battery Charger
Operate the butterfly and charge batteries on a sunny day. The batteries keep the circuit running for a while after the earth turns away from the sun, or when clouds pass over.

Stellar Fusion Collector Parts List

n	SS1-n	Solar cells or panels, combined for voltage as needed (see text)
1	D1	Diode, 1N4001
x	B1-x	NiCad Batteries, combine to match solar cell voltage (see text)
1	J1	Connector, 9V snap
1	B1-x	Battery Holder
.		Hookup wire
		Sunlight

A great source for solar products is:
REAL GOODS
966 Mazzoni Street
Ukiah, CA 95482-3471
Phone: 800-762-7325

Proportional Controller & Radio Control Interface

In this device, a Muscle Wire contracts to move a lever and a special low force position sensor. The sensor detects the wire's change in length and reports it to the interface circuit, made using the circuit board from a radio control (R/C) servo.

This circuit provides an excellent way to precisely control the position and motion of a Muscle Wire. This circuit receives control signals from a standard R/C receiver and can be positioned and trimmed like a standard R/C servo. Figure 3.50 shows the R/C circuit controlling a basic lever mechanism.

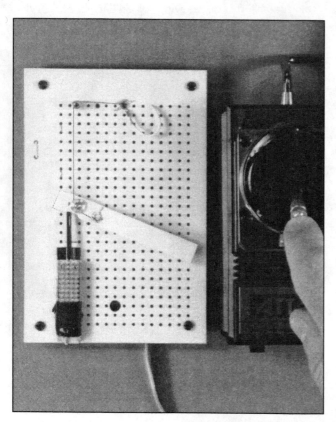
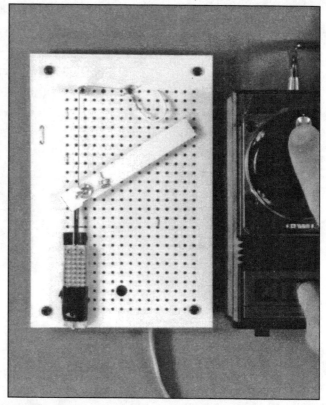

Figure 3.50   Project 13, Proportional Control Mechanism
This project demonstrates how a Muscle Wire with a position sensor can be controlled very precisely. Note that the Muscle Wire uses the most power when in the lowest position (left), and no power when at the highest position (right). Positions in between use power even if the lever is not moved.

Roger G. Gilbertson

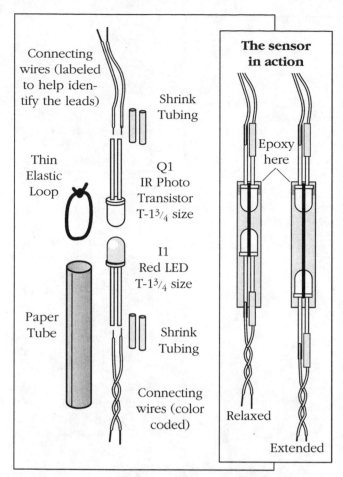

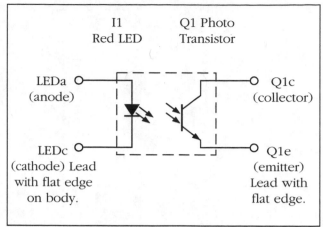

Figure 3.52   Schematic for Low Force Position Sensor
As the the distance between LED I1 and transistor Q1 increases, the intensity of the light reaching Q1 from the LED decreases, and changes Q1's resistance. A circuit like the one in Figure 3.56 can measure the resistance of Q1 and determines the change in position.

Figure 3.51   Parts and Assembly for Low Force Position Sensor
As the elastic band extends, the LED and transistor separate, reducing the light falling on the transistor and lowering its output signal. The force needed to extend the sensor is determined by the elastic band, and it can be changed by using other sizes of elastic.

Low Force Position Sensor Construction:

Tie a knot in a length of elastic to make a loop about 2 cm in diameter when relaxed. (For a sensor with more force, use several loops, larger elastic, or even a small spring.)

Solder insulated wires to each lead of LED I1 and the photo transistor Q1. Insulate the leads with shrink tubing or tape to prevent short circuits (Fig. 3.51).

Place Q1 on the elastic loop, locating the loop's knot between the leads of Q1, and secure it with a small amount of epoxy. Slip the LED I1 over the loop and locate it opposite Q1, leaving the elastic free to move.

Make a tube from thin paper (black or other opaque shade) to block unwanted light from the transistor Q1. Wrap the paper around a dowel or nail *slightly larger* than the outside of the transistor and LED and secure it with tape or glue.

Trim the tube to length (about 4 cm) and insert the Q1-I1-elastic assembly into the paper tube. Glue Q1 flush at one end of the tube, leaving the I1 end free to move as it is pulled (Fig. 3.51).

Low Force Position Sensor Parts List

1	I1	LED, Red, T-1$\frac{3}{4}$ size, (Jameco #94511)
1	Q1	IR Photo Transistor, NPN, T-1$\frac{3}{4}$ size, (Digi-Key #PN168PA)
4	J1-4	Thin connecting wire (#30 wire wrap wire or similar)
1	-	Elastic, small diameter, (available from a sewing supply store)
1	-	Tube, paper (see text)
		Shrink tubing
		Tape
		Epoxy

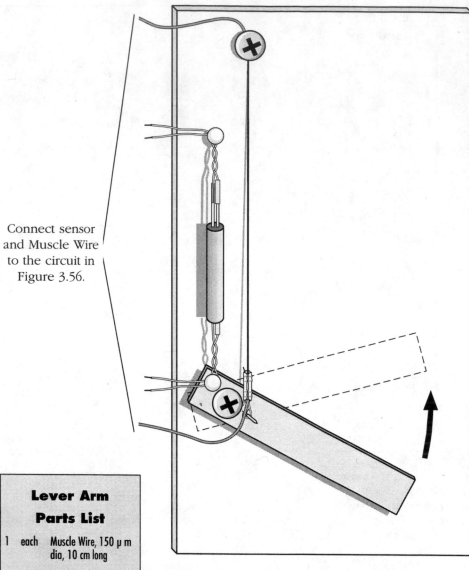

Connect sensor and Muscle Wire to the circuit in Figure 3.56.

Figure 3.54   Assembly for Proportional Control Lever
Assemble the Muscle Wire, crimp and connecting wire. Fabricate the lever arm and base from plastic sheet, positioning holes for the pivot, sensor and anchor screws. The low force position sensor provides the bias force for the Muscle Wire, and senses position when connected to the electronics in Figure 3.56.

Mechanism Construction:

Assemble the Muscle Wire, crimps, staples and connecting wires as shown in Figure 3.54. Use the dimensions given on the pattern sheet (page A-3) to make the lever arm.

For the best performance and reliability, make the arm and base from plastic sheet (like 2 mm styrene), and use screws for the pivot and to anchor the Muscle Wire. Position the lever on the base and connect the sensor to the lever arm. Pull on the sensor so that it exerts a slight force on the Muscle Wire.

Radio Control Interface Circuit Construction:

This circuit can be built using many common methods. To obtain the circuit board from a R/C servo, open the case and carefully remove all the interior parts. (This project uses an inexpensive Futaba "Attack" series system, and other systems will work as well.)

Make a sketch of the board noting the colors of the wires and where they connect, as your servo may be different from the one shown in Figure 3.55. Disconnect the motor and potentiometer from the printed circuit board by unsoldering the leads.

Build the supporting circuitry shown in Figure 3.56. Use perf board and solder construction for durability. Attach the position sensor and the Muscle Wire to the lever arm, and connect the circuit to a radio control receiver and battery pack as shown in Figure 3.56.

Testing:

Activate the R/C transmitter, receiver, and adjust VR1 on the circuit board to position the lever to a middle location.

Figure 3.55   Parts of a Typical Radio Control Servo
The servo's printed circuit board (PCB) contains sophisticated electronics that decode the signal from an R/C transmitter and control the position of the sensor by applying power to the motor. The circuit in Figure 3.56 adapts this PCB by replacing the servo's motor with a Muscle Wire, and the potentiometer with the low force position sensor. This results in a smaller and lighter R/C device for small and carefully controlled actions.

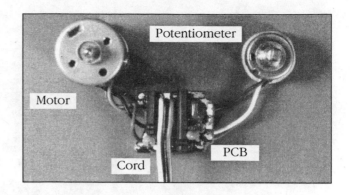

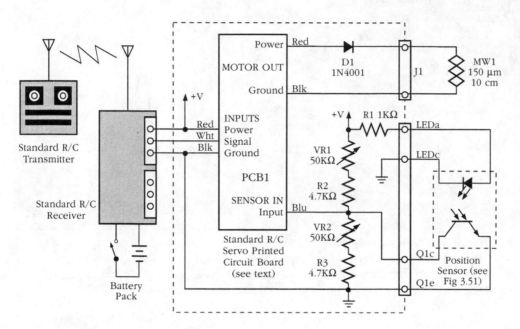

Figure 3.56   Schematic for R/C Interface Circuit
The power supply, receiver and servo circuit are from a standard R/C system. The other components connect the servo PCB (removed from a standard servo) to the low force position sensor (from Fig. 3.51), and the Muscle Wire on the lever arm (from Fig 3.54).

With the system powered, and with the joystick in the full UP position, adjust VR1 to place the lever arm at an appropriate maximum position.

Next move the joystick to the full DOWN position, and adjust VR2 to place the arm at a suitable minimum position (preferably where no power will be consumed). The lever arm should follow the action of the joystick, and the trim control on the transmitter should permit small adjustments in the lever's position.

How it Works:

The R/C servo circuit compares the signal from the R/C receiver with the signal from phototransistor Q1 and adjusts the output to the Muscle Wire, turning the current on or off to obtain the desired position, as measured by the sensor.

With a DC motor, changing the direction of the current reverses the motor's rotation. But a Muscle Wire will contract no matter which way the current flows.

Diode D1 limits the direction of current flow to the Muscle Wire, and permits it to contract only when powered in one way.

The sensor and circuit provide a feedback loop that holds the wire in a certain position by rapidly turning its power on and off. When powered, the Muscle Wire contracts and moves the lever, it separates I1 and Q1 in the position sensor, and the signal from Q1 changes. Potentiometers VR1 and VR2 per-

R/C Interface Parts List		
1	D1	Diode, 1N4001
1	R1	Res, 1K Ω, 1/4 W (Brn, Blk, Red, Gold)
2	R2,3	Res, 4.7K Ω, 1/4 W (Yel, Vio, Red, Gold)
2	VR1,2	Variable Resistor, 50K Ω, 1/2 W (Jameco #43107)
1	PCB1	Servo Printed Circuit Board (see text)
		Perf board
		Hook up wire

Plus a Radio Control Transmitter, Receiver, and Battery Pack for use with the Servo circuit.

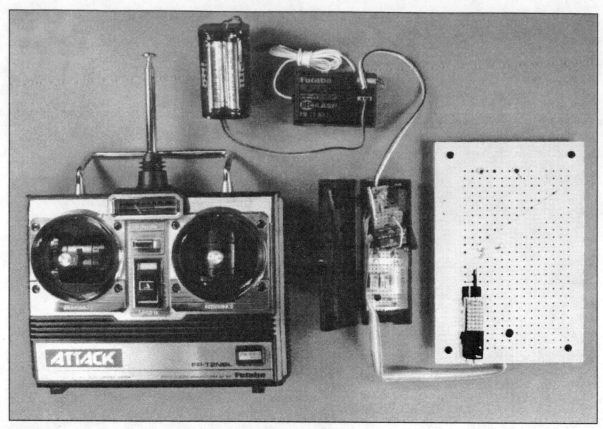

Figure 3.57 The R/C Proportional Control Circuit Demonstration
From left to right: two-channel radio control transmitter, battery pack for receiver and Muscle Wire servo, receiver, interface circuit using PCB from standard R/C servo mechanism, lever arm with low force position sensor (which, in the example above, was built inside a small flat pack rather than a tube).

mit fine tuning of the signal from the sensor. Note the circuit heats the Muscle Wire whenever it must hold a position, even if the wire is still.

The R/C servo circuit detects the modified signal from Q1, and when it corresponds to the signal from the receiver, the circuit reduces the power to the Muscle Wire.

Variations:

• Blow on the Muscle Wire and observe how the circuit quickly compensates for unexpected cooling of the wire.

• Make a latch for use inside an R/C plane that activates a Muscle Wire only when the joystick on the transmitter is pushed all the way "up" (i.e. adjust VR1 so the wire is nearly fully relaxed).

• To eliminate the need for an extra servo channel, wire the circuit to "listen in" on another channel by simply piggy-backing the power, ground, and signal lines onto the desired channel.

• Build an arm with several motions, each with its own low force position sensor and Muscle Wire, and control it from a multi-channel R/C transmitter.

• Add a Muscle Wire brake to clamp the lever in place whenever it is held in one position for a time. This permits the device to lock in place to save energy and yet still hold its position.

PROJECT 14

Multiple Wire Computer Interface Circuit

Figure 3.58   Multiple Wire Computer Interface Circuit
This controller connects to the serial port of a personal computer and can operate up to eight outputs and/or inputs. It can operate Muscle Wires, and sense limit switches, push buttons and the like. The interface can also run motors, solenoids, light bulbs and other devices, and can be programmed and left to run independent of the supporting computer.

This general purpose computer interface circuit uses a 8052 microcontroller IC to provide software based control of Muscle Wires from a personal computer via a standard serial port.

The circuit has outputs to activate typical driver circuits (as in Projects 6, 9 and 12), and has inputs for sensing push buttons, limit switches, etc.

The standard RS-232 serial port permits the board to connect to many common personal computers, and this project shows typical connections for IBM PC and the Apple Macintosh type machines. This interface circuit uses the computer as an input terminal and storage device.

The 8052 is a member of the 8051 family of microcontrollers, integrated circuits combining a microprocessor with memory and interface functions. The 8052 is an advanced integrated circuit containing an on-board inter-

Computer Interface Circuit Parts List

1	U1	IC, MAX232 Serial Int. (Jameco #24811)
1	U2	IC, 8052 µ controller (Jameco #125647)
1	U3	IC, 62256 Static RAM, 32K x 8 bytes, 100 ns (Jameco #42833)
1	U4	IC, 74LS373 Octal D-Type Latch (Jameco #47600)
1	R1	Res, 10K Ω, 1/4 W (Brn, Blk, Org, Gold)
1	R2	Res, 470 Ω, 1/4 W (Yel, Vio, Brn, Gold)
1	R3	Res, 8.2K Ω, 1/4 W (Gry, Red, Red, Gold)
6	C1-6	Cap, 10 µ F, 16 V min, alum. electrolytic
2	C7,8	Cap, 27 pF, 10 V min
2	C9,10	Cap, 0.01 µ F, 10 V min, ceramic
1	Q1	Transistor, 2N2907, PNP, Gen. Purpose
1	I1	LED, Red, T-1 size
1	Y1	Crystal, 12 MHz (Jameco #14402)
1	U1	Wire Wrap Socket, 16 pin DIP
1	U2	Wire Wrap Socket, 40 pin DIP
1	U3	Wire Wrap Socket, 28 pin DIP
1	U4	Wire Wrap Socket, 20 pin DIP
1	J1	Connector, 3 pin
1	J2	Connector, 2 pin polarized
1	SW1	Switch, Momentary
		Perf board
		Hook up wire
		Wire wrap wire

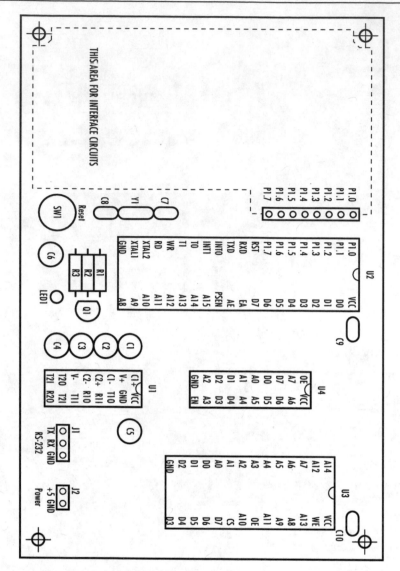

Perf Board Actual Size: 3" x 4.5"

Figure 3.59 Layout for Computer Interface Circuit
Position the components on the perf board, connect the power and ground distribution using heavier gauge hook up wire for good power distribution, then connect the data, address and signal lines with wire wrap wire.

preter for the BASIC computer language, 32K bytes (256K bits) of random access memory (RAM), 8K bytes of read only memory (ROM), binary coded decimal (BCD) floating-point math abilities, a real-time clock, and many other features, making it versatile and easy to use. For more information on this chip, consult the references on page 3-45.

To program the interface circuit, first type the program listing into a text file using a word processor on the computer. Then, using terminal emulation software, transfer the text file through the serial port into the interface circuit.

When the command "RUN" is sent to the

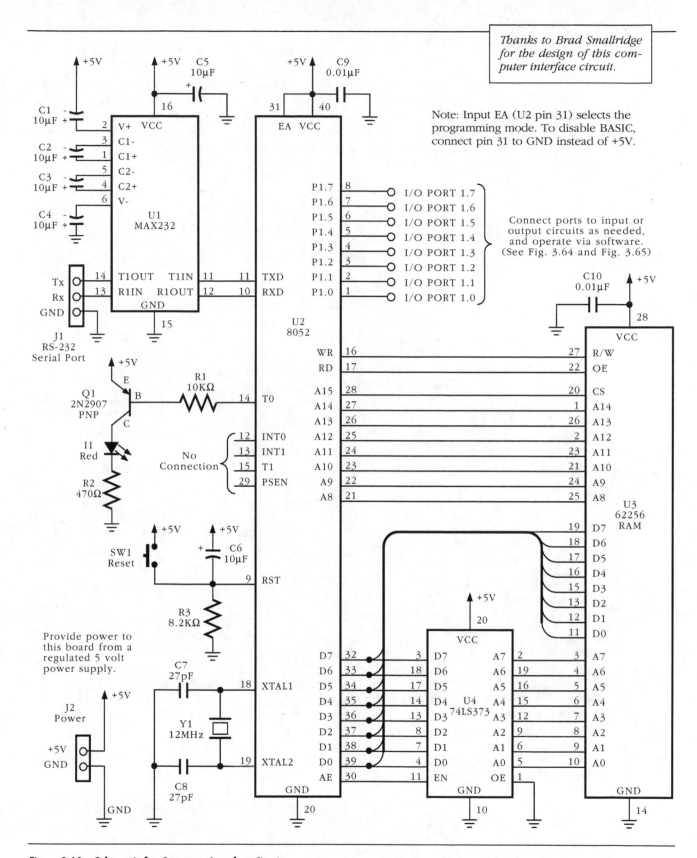

Thanks to Brad Smallridge for the design of this computer interface circuit.

Note: Input EA (U2 pin 31) selects the programming mode. To disable BASIC, connect pin 31 to GND instead of +5V.

Connect ports to input or output circuits as needed, and operate via software. (See Fig. 3.64 and Fig. 3.65)

Provide power to this board from a regulated 5 volt power supply.

Figure 3.60   Schematic for Computer Interface Circuit
Each of the eight I/O ports can be an input or output depending on the hardware and software associated with it.

microcontroller, the on-board BASIC interpreter will process the code (checking it for any errors or typos) and execute the instructions.

Each of the 8052's I/O (input-output) ports can be individually "written to" (turned on or off), or "read from" (sensed).

This project includes hardware to connect to the I/O ports that lets the circuit activate devices as outputs (see Figure 3.64) and detect positions and switch closures as inputs (see Figure 3.65).

Assembly:

This circuit should be built using wire wrap for the many data, address and signal connections, and a heavier wire wrap, or hook up wire for good power and ground distribution. Position the components on the perf board as shown in Figure 3.59 and connect them following the schematic in Figure 3.60.

Leave the integrated circuits (ICs) in protective anti-static foam until the board is complete. Then, double check all connections and install the ICs, noting their proper orientation.

Serial Cable:

Build or obtain a cable appropriate to your computer. Figures 3.61 shows a typical serial connection for the printer or modem ports on a Macintosh computer. It uses a Mini DIN-8 plug, available from some electronics suppliers (see the references section) or by adapting an appropriate printer cable.

Figure 3.62 shows a typical serial connection for IBM PC-type computers, using D-25 and D-9 type connectors.

Interface Testing:

When you have completed the assembly of the interface board and serial cable, and have double checked all connections, attach the interface to the computer with the cable.

On the computer, run a terminal emulation or

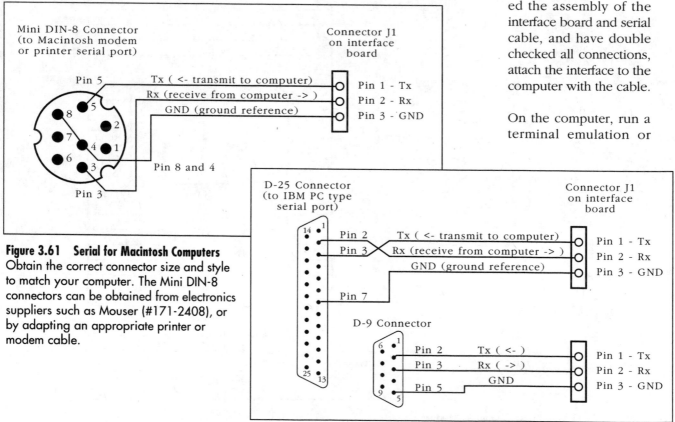

Figure 3.61 Serial for Macintosh Computers Obtain the correct connector size and style to match your computer. The Mini DIN-8 connectors can be obtained from electronics suppliers such as Mouser (#171-2408), or by adapting an appropriate printer or modem cable.

Figure 3.62 Serial for IBM PC-type Computers For both 25 and 9 pin ports.

other communications program, set for the correct serial port and 8 bits, no parity, 1 stop bit, baud rate up to 9600.

Power the interface board using a regulated 5 volt power supply. The LED on the interface should not light at this time.

On the computer, press the space bar. This sends a single space character to the interface, and it should respond with:

```
*MCS-51(tm) BASIC V1.1*
READY
>
```

Congratulations, its alive!

If the board does not respond, check the terminal program for proper settings, the cable for correct Tx and Rx connections (try switching them), and the interface

board for proper connections, incorrect or misplaced parts, etc.

Debugging the board can become a little involved, but patience and persistence will pay off. Consult the references listed on page 3-45 for more on the 8052.

With the interface board operating, enter Test Program One (Fig. 3-63) to flash the LED. This can be typed in as a text file and down loaded to the interface, or typed directly in from the terminal program.

When you have successfully completed the simple test of the interface board, add an output circuit as shown in Figure 3.64 to permit the board to activate a Muscle Wire. Adding an input circuit (Fig. 3.65) permits the software to receive a

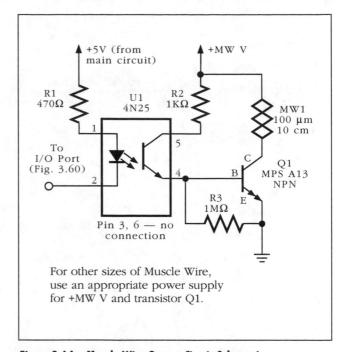

Figure 3.64 Muscle Wire Output Circuit Schematic
This circuit can be added to the interface board in Figure 3.60 and connects to an available I/O port on the 8052.

signal from a switch, push button or other sensor. Test Program Two (Fig. 3.66) shows a simple program that reads Ports 1.0 through 1.03, and when it detects a switch closure, it activates Port 1.4 through 1.7 to drive Muscle Wires in different ways.

Starting with the commands shown in Test Program Two, and the circuits in Figures 3.64 and 3.65, you create your own software and hardware customized to your projects.

The eight I/O ports on the interface board can function as either inputs or outputs, allowing the board to drive eight

```
    NEW

10      REM TEST PROGRAM ONE - 9102.21 rev 9207.01
20      REM Requires Jumper from I/O P1.0 to input T0
30      R=50 : REM Delay Count
40      REM Start

100     PORT1=PORT1.OR.01H : REM Turn LED Off
110     GOSUB 160 : REM Delay
120     PORT1=PORT1.AND.0FEH : REM Turn LED On
130     GOSUB 160 : REM Delay
140     GOTO 100 : REM Repeat

150     REM Delay Subroutine
160     FOR X=1 TO R
170     NEXT X
180     RETURN

    RUN
```

Figure 3.63 Listing for Test Program One
Use this program as a first test of the completed interface. The LED I1 will flash at about 2 Hz with R=50 and about 1 Hz with R=100. NOTE: Connect a jumper wire from U2 pin 1 (I/O Port 1.0) to U2 pin 14 (the T0 interrupt input).

Muscle Wire Output Circuit Parts List		
1	U1	IC, 4N25 Optoisolator (Jameco #40985)
1	R1	Res, 470 Ω, 1/4 W (Yel, Vio, Brn, Gold)
1	R2	Res, 1K Ω, 1/4 W (Brn, Blk, Red, Gold)
1	R3	Res, 1M Ω, 1/4 W (Brn, Blk, Grn, Gold)
1	Q1	Trans, MPS A13 NPN, Darl. Amp. (Jameco #26489)
1	U1	Wire Wrap Socket, 6 pin DIP
		Muscle Wire, as needed
		Hookup wire
		Wire wrap wire

Muscle Wires, read eight switches, or any combination of the two.

How it Works:

Integrated circuit U1, the MAX232 serial communications chip, receives and transmits signals to and from the interface board. The four capacitors, C1-C4, help generate the higher voltages required by the RS-232 standard, without needing a multiple voltage power supply (a big advantage).

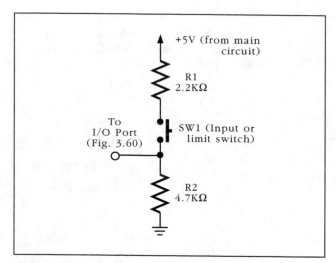

Figure 3.65   Switch Input Circuit Schematic
This circuit can be added to the interface board in Figure 3.60 and connects to an available I/O port on the 8052.

U2, the 8052 microcontroller, contains a central processing unit (CPU), memory, real-time clock and input/output hardware, as well as a BASIC language interpreter. It reads inputs and directs outputs according to the the software loaded into memory via the RS-232 serial port.

U3, the static random access memory (SRAM), provides storage for 32K 8-bit bytes (32,768 x 8 or 262,144 separate ones and zeros) of data and instructions.

The 8052 microcontroller selects individual memory locations via the address bus (lines A0-A15), and reads and writes to memory via the data bus (lines D0-D7).

U4, the 74LS373 contains eight latches to help the microcontroller address the memory chip U3. Crystal Y1 and capacitors C7 and C8 provide a stable 12 MHz oscillating reference for the microprocessor.

Resistor R1 limits the current from U2 output T0 to the base of transistor Q1. When T0 is high, Q1 turns on, letting current flow through LED I1 and R2, which limits the current to protect the LED.

When the interface board is first powered up, capacitor C6 and resistor R3 hold the Reset input of U2 (RST, pin 9) high for a few seconds. This permits the power levels on the board to stabilize before the controller starts operating.

Pressing switch SW1 produces a manual reset, useful in case the chip "hangs" for some reason. Capacitors C5, C9 and C10 protect their associated ICs from electrical noise. They should be installed

as close to the IC sockets as possible.

Variations:

• Expand the hardware and software shown here to make more sophisticated projects including robot arms, computer controlled railroad displays, animated motion effects, or an automated Muscle Wire project testing lab, to name a few.

• Build four Muscle Wire devices (such as Projects 1 through 4) and operate them all from a computer, cycling them at different rates, or activating them with four different input buttons.

• Build a robot arm with gripper, elbow and shoulder based on lever mechanisms (Projects 2 and 13) and controlled from the interface. Use limit switches, optical position sensors (as in Figure 3.51) or magnetic Hall Effect sensors to detect the position of each joint.

• Build a stand-alone controller to activate a sequence of Muscle Wires at the press of a switch. Use it to animate a display or diorama when a viewer pushes a button, or to make a sequence of actions for animated motion picture effects or magic illusions.

• Use this board to operate Boris the motorless walking machine in Project 15.

```
NEW

10      REM TEST PROGRAM TWO - 9102.18 rev 9207.01
20      REM
30      REM * * * * * * * * * * * * * * * * * * * * * * * * * * * *
32      REM   Program uses PORT1.0 through PORT1.3 as inputs (buttons, etc.)
34      REM   and PORT1.4 through PORT1.7 as outputs (Muscle Wires, LEDS, etc.)
36      REM   with each IN performing a different output function:
38      REM     IN1 (PORT1.0) activates OUT1 (PORT1.4) while held ON
40      REM     IN2 (PORT1.1) turns on OUT2 (PORT1.5) for a preset time (CVAL)
42      REM     IN3 (PORT1.2) toggles OUT3 (PORT1.6) ON and OFF
46      REM     IN4 (PORT1.3) master ON, same as pressing IN1, IN2, and IN3
48      REM * * * * * * * * * * * * * * * * * * * * * * * * * * * *
60      REM SETUP
70      PORT1 = 0FH : REM !!! ALWAYS KEEP INPUTS SET TO 1 !!!
80      CVAL1 = 15 : REM IN2 DELAY VALUE
90      OUT1 = 0 : OUT2 = 0 : OUT3 = 0 : OUT4 = 0

100     REM START MAIN LOOP
105     REM READ PORT1.0-1.3, IF TRUE (ON) THEN MAKE INn = 1, ELSE MAKE 0
110     IF (PORT1.AND.01H) THEN IN1 = 1 ELSE IN1 = 0 : REM READ PORT1.0
120     IF (PORT1.AND.02H) THEN IN2 = 1 ELSE IN2 = 0 : REM READ PORT1.1
130     IF (PORT1.AND.04H) THEN IN3 = 1 ELSE IN3 = 0 : REM READ PORT1.2
140     IF (PORT1.AND.08H) THEN IN4 = 1 ELSE IN4 = 0 : REM READ PORT1.3
200     REM CHECK EACH INPUT AND PREPARE OUT
210     GOSUB 4000 : REM SET OUT4
220     GOSUB 3000 : REM SET OUT3
230     GOSUB 2000 : REM SET OUT2
240     GOSUB 1000 : REM SET OUT1
300     REM PREPARE AND WRITE OUTPUT
310     OUT = 0FH : REM CLEAR OUT
320     IF OUT1 = 1 OUT = (OUT.OR.1FH) : REM SET PORT1.4 ON
330     IF OUT2 = 1 OUT = (OUT.OR.2FH) : REM SET PORT1.5 ON
340     IF OUT3 = 1 OUT = (OUT.OR.4FH) : REM SET PORT1.6 ON
350     IF OUT4 = 1 OUT = (OUT.OR.8FH) : REM SET PORT1.7 ON
360     PORT1 = OUT : REM WRITE OUTPUT TO PORT1.4-1.7
900     REM END MAIN LOOP
990     GOTO 100 : REM REPEAT

999     REM SUBROUTINES

1000    REM PREPARE OUT1
1010    REM IF IN1 ON, OUT1 ON
1100    IF IN1 = 1 THEN OUT1 = 1 ELSE OUT1 = 0
1900    RETURN

2000    REM PREPARE OUT2
2010    REM IF IN2 PRESSED, THEN COUNTDOWN
2100    IF COUNTFLAG = 1 THEN GOTO 2300 : REM GOTO COUNT.FINISHED
2110    COUNTER = CVAL1 : REM SET THE COUNTER
2120    IF IN2 = 1 THEN COUNTFLAG = 1 : REM IF PRESSED START COUNTER
2190    RETURN
2300    REM COUNTDOWN
2310    IF COUNTER = 0 THEN GOTO 2500 : REM GOTO COUNTDONE
2320    OUT2 = 1 : REM IF STILL COUNTING, OUT2 ON
2330    COUNTER = COUNTER-1 : REM DECREMENT COUNTER
2340    RETURN
2500    REM COUNT.FINISHED
2510    OUT2 = 0 : REM IF DONE COUNTING, OUT2 OFF
2520    COUNTFLAG = 0 : REM CLEAR COUNTFLAG
2900    RETURN

3000    REM PREPARE OUT3
3010    REM PRESS ON, PRESS AGAIN OFF
3100    IF IN3 = 0 THEN GOTO 3300 : REM GOTO MAINTAIN
3110    IF IN3 = OLDIN3 GOTO 3300 : GOTO MAINTAIN
3120    IF OUT3 = 1 GOTO 3500 : REM GOTO OUT3.OFF
3130    IF OUT3 = 0 GOTO 3700 : REM GOTO OUT3.ON
3300    REM MAINTAIN
3310    OLDIN3 = IN3 : REM REMEMBER IN3 FOR NEXT TIME
3320    RETURN
3500    REM OUT3.OFF
3510    OUT3 = 0 : REM TURN OFF
3520    OLDIN3 = IN3 : REM REMEMBER IN3 FOR NEXT TIME
3530    RETURN
3700    REM OUT3.ON
3710    OUT3 = 1 : REM TURN ON
3720    OLDIN3 = IN3 : REM REMEMBER IN3 FOR NEXT TIME
3900    RETURN

4000    REM PREPARE OUT4
4010    REM MASTER INPUT
4020    REM SAME AS PRESSING INPUTS 1-3
4100    REM SET IN1, IN2 & IN3 ON
4110    IF IN4 = 0 RETURN
4120    IN1 = 1 : IN2 = 1 : IN3 = 1 : REM SET IN1-3 ON
4900    RETURN

RUN
```

Figure 3.66 Listing for Test Program Two
Enter this program as a text file in a word processing program, then use a tele-communications program to down load it via the serial port to the 8052 interface board. Having the program stored as a text file permits it to be printed, modified and reloaded without extensive retyping. Use the instructions shown here to write your own software for running a variety of Muscle Wire devices.

Additional References:

These two books give more information about the operation and programming of the 8052 microcontroller.

BASIC-52 – A Complete Reference to Programming 80C52-BASIC
> Systronix, Inc.
> 555 South 300 East #21
> Salt Lake City, UT 84111
>> Phone: 801-534-1017
>> Fax: 801-534-1019
>> Web:

Embedded Microcontroller and Processor Handbook, #270645
> Intel Corp.
> Literature Distribution
> 1000 Business Center Drive
> Mt. Prospect, IL 60056
>> Phone: 800-628-8686
>> Web:

Micromint supplies various 8052 circuit boards and information.
> Micromint, Inc.
> 4 Park Street
> Vernon, CT 06066
>> Phone: 203-871-6170
>> Web:

Plus, text files of these BASIC software programs and more are available from the Mondo-tronics web site:
http://www.Mondo.com/mwpb/

BORIS –
A Motorless Six Legged
Walking Machine

Figure 3.67   Project 15, *Boris*, A Motorless Six Legged Walker
Following in the footsteps of larger and more sophisticated walking machines (like *Genghis* and *Attila* from MIT), *Boris* presents an exciting and low cost project that can be up and "running" quickly. And because Boris uses motorless Muscle Wire technology it has great potential for expansion and adaptation in many ways.

After you understand and have practiced the basics of how to connect, power and utilize the strength of Muscle Wires as shown in the previous projects, you're ready to build Boris, our tiny, motorless walking machine.

Boris moves with an amazingly smooth and lifelike action, taking steps about one centimeter long and one centimeter high.

Boris's simple design uses eight separate Muscle Wires to create all mo-

tions; one to make the forward/backward motion on each of the legs, and two wires for lifting alternating legs with each step. Build Boris from piano wire, balsa wood or foam core, and plastic sheet. Connect Boris via a

Roger G. Gilbertson

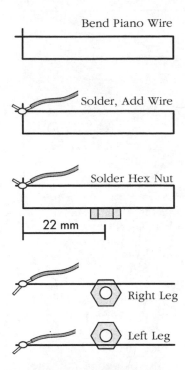

Bend Piano Wire

Solder, Add Wire

Solder Hex Nut

22 mm

Right Leg

Left Leg

Figure 3.68 Leg Components
Thin piano wire provides both structure and a bias force for each leg. Note position of nut for left and right side legs.

lightweight wire wrap wire harness to an interface circuit that accepts signals from the parallel printer port of a PC-type computer. Then operate Boris from the computer's keyboard.

Assemble Boris

Cut and bend the thin piano wire (a very springy steel wire available at hobby stores) into the rectangle shown in the Pattern Sheet (page A-3). Solder the rectangle closed using silver solder and its flux (available at hobby and craft stores).

The flux cleans the wire for a solid bond. Follow

its instructions and observe all safety precautions. When soldering, tape the parts down to hold them. In the same joint solder a 12 cm length of insulated wire wrap wire as shown. Repeat for six rectangles.

Solder a hex nut to a wire rectangle (Fig 3.68), placing it as shown. Hold the pieces in place with tape on a cardboard or wood base, and use silver solder and flux. Make three left and three right legs. Be sure to not let any solder run inside the threads of the nut.

For the ten remaining hex nuts, solder a 12 cm length wire wrap wire to each, as in Figure 3.69.

Make the three leg modules from balsa wood or foam core, with slots and holes as shown on the Pattern Sheet (page A-3).

Place left and right wire rectangles into the leg modules, locating the hex nuts as shown (Fig 3.70). The top and bottom of the wire should be flush with the surface of the foam. Glue them in place with a "5-minute" type epoxy. Repeat to make three identical leg modules.

Prepare the ten hex nuts (the ones with wires soldered to them) by covering the hole on each nut with a narrow strip of tape to prevent epoxy from getting into their threads. Repeat for both sides of all ten nuts.

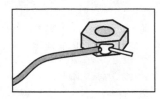

Figure 3.69 Solder Wires
Be sure to not let solder run inside the nut. (If this happens, replace the nut.)

12 mm

Figure 3.70 Leg Module Assembly
Insert two wire rectangles into the slots in the leg module square. The nuts must be located 12 mm from the edge, as shown. Epoxy the wires in place.

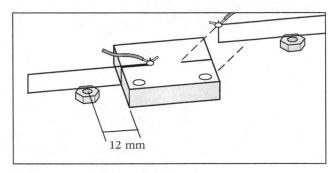

Cover hole with tape

Figure 3.71 Epoxy the Hex Nuts to the Leg Module
Do not get glue inside the nut or the hole below it.

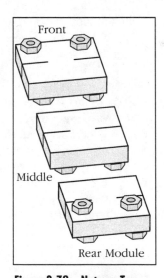

Front

Middle

Rear Module

Figure 3.72 Nuts on Top
Locate nuts on the front and rear modules only, and epoxy in place.

Boris Parts List	
70 cm	Piano wire, 0.38 mm (0.015") dia
14 cm	Piano wire, 1.25 mm (0.050") dia.
16 each	Hex nuts, 4-40
16 each	Screws, 4-40, 1/8"
12 cm	Plastic tube, 3 mm (0.125") OD, 1.5 mm (0.062") ID
36 cm	Plastic tube, 2.5 mm (0.10") OD, 1.25 mm (0.050") ID
60 cm	Muscle Wire, 100 μm dia. Cut as needed.
1 each	Header, 8 pin, 2.5 mm (0.100") spacing
	Balsa wood or foam core, 6 mm (0.25") thick
	Plastic sheet, 1.25 mm (0.050") thk.
	Wire wrap wire
	Silver solder and Flux
	Epoxy, 5 minute type

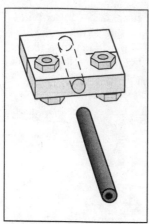

Figure 3.73 Insert the Large Plastic Tube
Glue tube in place with epoxy, centering it in the foam core. Repeat for all three leg modules.

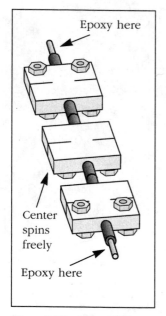

Figure 3.74 Place All Three Leg Modules on Center Rod
With epoxy glue the front and back modules to the rod, spacing them slightly apart so the center module can rotate freely. (Wires omitted for clarity.)

Epoxy a hex nut to the foam core leg module, over a pre-cut hole as in Fig 3.71. Repeat for the second hole on the same side, and all three leg modules.

Use care not to get epoxy in the holes on the leg module or inside the hex nut. If epoxy should get on top of the nut, wipe off the excess, then when fully hardened, sand the top of the nuts with fine sandpaper.

Epoxy another two hex nuts to the foam core, on the opposite side from the other nuts, on just the front and back leg modules (Fig 3.72). Remove the protective tape from all the hex nuts.

Into the hole that runs through the center of each leg module, insert a 4 cm long 3 mm diameter plastic tube, centering it so both ends extend the same amount, and epoxy in place (Fig 3.73). Repeat for all three modules.

Slide the three leg modules on to the 14 cm long piano wire center rod, orienting each as in Figure 3.74. Let the rod extend evenly from each end and epoxy it to the front and back modules. Adjust for a small amount of space (0.5 mm) so the center module can spin freely.

Cut out the leg panels from 1.25 mm sheet plastic and epoxy them to the wire rectangles (Fig 3.75).

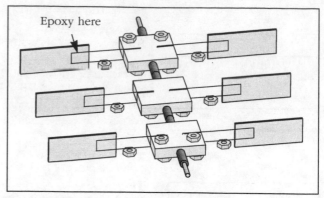

Figure 3.75 Attach Leg Panels with Epoxy
Hold the leg panels in place with tape until the epoxy hardens. Be sure they are all square and even to each other. (Electrical wires omitted for clarity.)

Hold them with tape until the epoxy hardens. Be sure they are parallel and even to each other.

Place the whole assembly on a spacer like the cassette boxes and pencils in Fig. 3.76. Tape the 5 cm long leg tubes to the leg panels, as shown. Adjust the tubes up and down so they all contact the

table surface with the leg modules resting flat on the pencils. Glue the tubes to the panels with epoxy or a solvent glue.

Form the Spacer Block (as on the Pattern sheet) from balsa wood or foam core, and glue to the middle leg module (Fig 3.77). Epoxy two 1 cm long segments of tube to the top of the

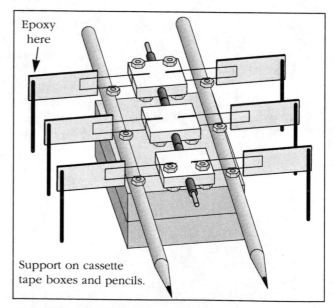

Figure 3.76 Attach Leg Tubes with Epoxy
Place the assembly on a supporting block and adjust so all legs are the same length. Hold tubes with tape until dry.

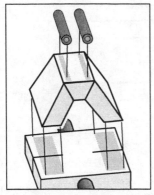

Figure 3.77   Spacer Block
Form the spacer block and epoxy it and two tubes to the middle leg module.

block. Let it rest until all glue has hardened.

Install the Muscle Wires

Install screws in all sixteen hex nuts. Attach a length of 100 μm diameter Muscle Wire to one of the legs by catching it between the nut and screw.

Tug on the Muscle Wire and position it under the screw on the OPPOSITE side of the module, as in Figure 3.78. Keep enough tension on the wire to bend the leg about five degrees, then tighten the screw to secure the wire. This tension provides the bias force needed to ex-

tend the Muscle Wire after it cools. Trim the wire, leaving about 1 cm extra for later adjustment and repeat for all legs.

On each module, note how the wire pairs cross. To prevent them from short circuiting, separate them with a 1 cm by 2 cm slip of paper held with tape, as in Figure 3.78.

On the top side, attach a length of Muscle Wire for the left side and right side lift, as in Figure 3.79. Note that these wires pass through the short tubes on the spacer block, and *do not* cross. Adjust these wires so they have just enough slack to let the middle leg module move up or down about 1 cm, as measured at the feet.

Electrical Wiring

To prevent confusion and incorrect wiring, review the diagrams, and double check each connection carefully, both before and after making it. Note that the electrical wires connect to the 8-pin header block, permitting easy connection of the robot to the interface circuit described below.

Figure 3.81 shows Boris's physical and electrical connections. Connect the wires as listed in the table. Note that the center rod acts as a common power supply to all the Muscle Wires. Double check all connections.

Interface Circuit

Build the circuit in figure 3.82 and 3.83. It receives signals from a computer's parallel printer port and provides an adjustable voltage to Boris's Muscle Wires. Build the circuit with the wire wrap or perf board methods.

Build the harness with seven wire wrap wires, each about 1 meter long. Bundle them together with small lengths of wire wrap wire or with loops of thread

When assembled, test the circuit, carefully measuring and adjusting the output before attaching it to Boris. Start a BASIC program, then enter and run Program Three (Fig. 3.84). Leaving switch SW1 *off* until all signals have been checked, test that each bit can be turned on and off from the keyboard.

At this point you may wish to connect Boris and test each action. This provides a good way to check for correct wiring, power levels, and proper leg actions.

Finally, run Program Four (Fig. 3.85), connect Boris, and *watch it walk!*

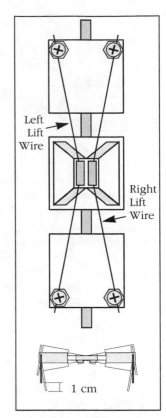

Figure 3.79   Lift Wires
These wires pull the middle leg module from side to side to make the leg lifting action. Leave just enough slack so the legs move up and down about 1 cm.

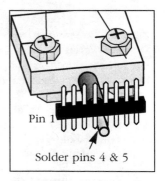

Figure 3.80   Attach Header
Solder pins 4 and 5 to center rod for a good electrical connection and a solid physical one, too.

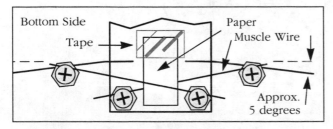

Figure 3.78   Install the Muscle Wires on the Legs
Catch the wire under the screw head, and tense it to bend the leg a bit, as shown. Insulate with paper slip.

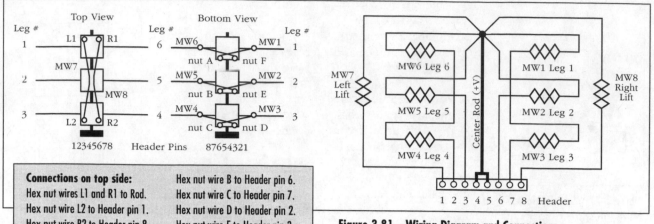

Connections on top side:
Hex nut wires L1 and R1 to Rod.
Hex nut wire L2 to Header pin 1.
Hex nut wire R2 to Header pin 8.

Connections on bottom side:
Hex nut wire A to Leg wire 3.

Hex nut wire B to Header pin 6.
Hex nut wire C to Header pin 7.
Hex nut wire D to Header pin 2.
Hex nut wire E to Header pin 3.
Hex nut wire F to Leg wire 4.
Leg wires 1, 2, 5 and 6 to Rod.
Solder Header pins 4 & 5 to Rod.

Figure 3.81   Wiring Diagram and Connections
Viewing Boris from above, number the legs from 1 to 6 like an integrated circuit, as shown. The schematic shows the six leg wires, and two lift wires. Header pins 4 and 5 connect to the center rod which powers all Muscle Wires.

How it Works:

When the BASIC software running in the computer sends a command to the parallel port, it creates a pattern of eight bits, which the parallel port represents as voltages on eight wires (D0 through D7). A high signal (near +5 Volts) represents a 1, and a low voltage (near 0 Volts) represents a zero.

The BASIC command "LPRINT CHR$(bits);" sends a single character of eight ones and zeros. The actual pattern depends on the number entered for "bits", from 0 to 255. The semicolon (;) at the end of the command line holds, or "latches", the bit pattern on the port. (If the LPRINT command line did not end in a semicolon, the program would send a Line Feed and a

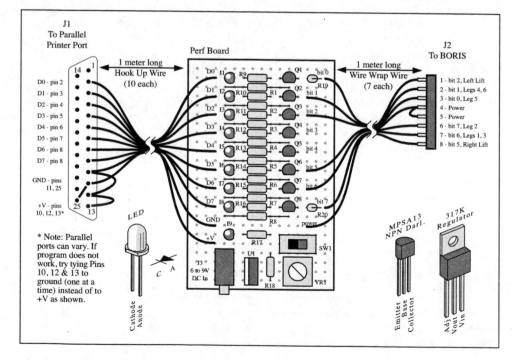

Figure 3.82   Boris Interface Circuit and Cables
Use this component layout to easily connect the parts as shown in Figure 3.83. Connect J1 to the parallel port on a PC-type computer and connect J2 to Boris. Power the circuit with a 6 to 9 V DC supply, and adjust the variable resistor VR1 to set the power level to the Muscle Wires. LEDs I1-8 show the bit pattern on the parallel port.

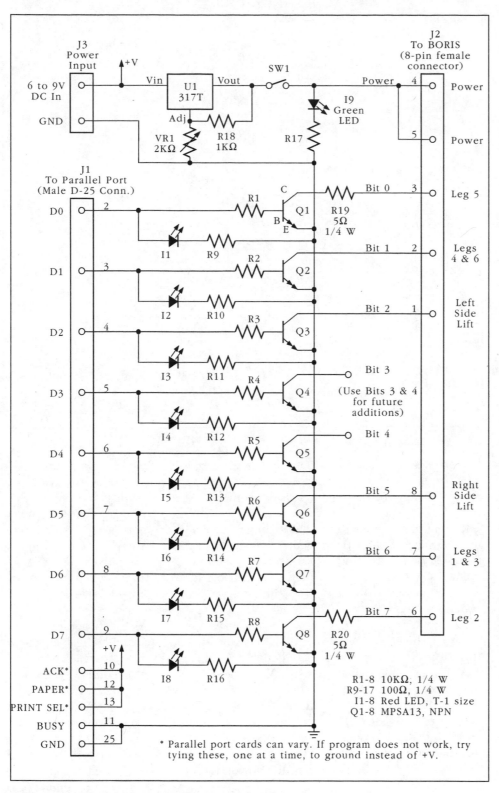

Parallel Port Interface Circuit Parts List

Qty	Ref	Description
8	R1-8	Resistor, 10KΩ, 1/4 W (Brn, Blk, Org, Gold)
9	R9-17	Resistor, 100Ω, 1/4 W (Brn, Blk, Brn, Gold)
1	R18	Resistor, 1KΩ, 1/4 W (Brn, Blk, Red, Gold)
2	R19,20	Resistor, 5Ω, 1/4 W (Grn, Blk, Gold, Gold)
1	VR1	Variable Resistor, 2KΩ, 1/4W
8	I1-8	LED, Red, T-1 size
1	I9	LED, Green, T-1 size
8	Q1-8	Transistor, MPS A13 NPN, Darl. Amp. (Jameco #26489)
1	U1	IC, 317T Regulator (Jameco #23579)
1	SW1	Switch, SPST (Single Pole Single Throw)
1	J1	Connector, D-25 male
1	J2	Connector, 8 pin SIP (or half a 16 pin DIP socket)
1	J3	Connector, Power Jack (as needed)
8 meters		Wire Wrap Wire
9 meters		Hookup Wire
		Perf Board (see Figure 3.82)
		Solder

R1-8 10KΩ, 1/4 W
R9-17 100Ω, 1/4 W
I1-8 Red LED, T-1 size
Q1-8 MPSA13, NPN

* Parallel port cards can vary. If program does not work, try tying these, one at a time, to ground instead of +V.

Figure 3.83 Schematic for Parallel Port Interface Circuit
This circuit captures the bit pattern from a standard PC-type parallel port and displays it with LEDs (ON = 1, OFF = 0). Also, each transistor, Q1 to Q8, provides power to drive a Muscle Wire when its corresponding bit is high. Boris uses six of the eight circuits. Output Bits 3 and 4 remain free for future additions (grippers, feelers, pointing mechanisms, etc.).

```
          NEW

          10    REM Test Program Three - Blip A Line
          11    REM 9210.19 Rev 9304.31
          12    REM Activate a line on the parallel port for short time
          13    REM
          14    REM   Keyboard   Output    BORIS
          15    REM   "1" Key  =  Bit 0  =  Leg 5
          16    REM   "2" Key  =  Bit 1  =  Legs 4 & 6
          17    REM   "3" Key  =  Bit 2  =  Left Side Lift
          18    REM   "4" Key  =  Bit 3  =  not used
          19    REM   "5" Key  =  Bit 4  =  not used
          20    REM   "6" Key  =  Bit 5  =  Right Side Lift
          21    REM   "7" Key  =  Bit 6  =  Legs 1 & 3
          22    REM   "8" Key  =  Bit 7  =  Leg 2
          23    REM

          30    DELAY = 200: REM Delay ON time, Increase for longer
          40    LPRINT CHR$(0); : REM Clear port
          50    PRINT "Press 1 thru 8 to activate bits, Q to end"

          100   A$ = INKEY$: REM Get key press
          110   IF A$ = "1" THEN LPRINT CHR$(1); : GOTO 200: REM bit 0
          120   IF A$ = "2" THEN LPRINT CHR$(2); : GOTO 200: REM bit 1
          130   IF A$ = "3" THEN LPRINT CHR$(4); : GOTO 200: REM bit 2
          140   IF A$ = "4" THEN LPRINT CHR$(8); : GOTO 200: REM bit 3
          150   IF A$ = "5" THEN LPRINT CHR$(16); : GOTO 200: REM bit 4
          160   IF A$ = "6" THEN LPRINT CHR$(32); : GOTO 200: REM bit 5
          170   IF A$ = "7" THEN LPRINT CHR$(64); : GOTO 200: REM bit 6
          180   IF A$ = "8" THEN LPRINT CHR$(128); : GOTO 200: REM bit 7
          190   IF A$ = "q" OR A$ = "Q" THEN LPRINT CHR$(0); : END
          195   GOTO 100

          200   REM Delay loop
          210   FOR I = 1 TO DELAY
          220   NEXT I
          230   LPRINT CHR$(0); : REM After delay, clear output
          240   GOTO 100

          RUN
```

Carriage Return character, which would confuse the robot's walking pattern.)

The eight bits connect to the interface through J1, the D-25 connector, and eight hook up wires. A ninth wire provides a common ground between the computer and board. Each of the eight bits functions in the same way. For example, when Bit D0 goes high, it causes LED I1 to glow, and turns on transistor Q1 which provides power, via the wire wrap wire harness, to Leg 5 of Boris.

Resistors R19 and R20 equalize the total resistance of the circuits for Legs 2 and 5. Without them, the lower resistance would prevent full contraction of other Muscle Wires when activating two or more circuits together. Resistors R1 to R8 limit the base current of the transistors, and R9 to R16 limit the current through LEDs I1 to I8.

The 317T regulator, U1, together with variable resistor VR1 and resistor R18, controls the voltage from the power supply connected at J3. Adjust VR1 to increase or decrease the voltage, and thus the power, to Boris.

Caution: Unwanted bit patterns may appear on the parallel port when first turning on the computer or when running other programs. Use SW1 as a "safety switch" to turn Boris's power OFF when not in use. With switch SW1 ON, LED I9 lights, and power flows to Boris as directed by the incoming bit pattern.

As the program runs, it changes the bit patterns at the parallel port, activating different transistors, which in turn activate the various Muscle Wires and make Boris walk.

With properly timed and sequenced patterns of bits (like Test Program Four), Boris can walk forward, go in reverse, and turn in either direction at your command!

```
NEW

10    REM Test Program Four - RG 9305.11
11    REM Walking Program for BORIS Connected to PC Parallel Port
12    REM Control from numeric keypad: UP arrow = Forward, etc.
13    REM
14    REM    Send bits to the parallel port with   LPRINT CHR$(Bits);
15    REM
16    REM    Bits = 1*n + 2*n + 4*n + 8*n + 16*n + 32*n + 64*n + 128*n
17    REM
18    REM Bits equation sets bits ON if n = 1 or OFF if n = 0
19    REM    First position (1*n) is bit 0
20    REM    Last position (128*n) is bit 7
21    REM Calculate with each n to 1 or 0 for other output patterns
22    REM
23    REM Note: Ending semicolon (;) on LPRINT command holds
24    REM         bit pattern at parallel port until next LPRINT
25    REM

30    DELAY = 350: REM Increase for slower walk, decrease for faster

40    PRINT "Press keypad arrow keys for Fwd, Back, Left, Right"
50    PRINT "Press space bar for Stop"
60    PRINT "Press Q at any time to Quit"

100   REM Stop walking
110   LPRINT CHR$(0);     : GOSUB 1000: REM Clear All Bits
120   GOTO 100

200   REM Walk Forward
210   LPRINT CHR$(65);    : GOSUB 1000: REM Bit 6, 0 ON
220   LPRINT CHR$(4);     : GOSUB 1000: REM Bit 2 ON
230   LPRINT CHR$(130);   : GOSUB 1000: REM Bit 7, 1 ON
240   LPRINT CHR$(32);    : GOSUB 1000: REM Bit 5 ON
250   GOTO 200

300   REM Walk Reverse
310   LPRINT CHR$(65);    : GOSUB 1000: REM Bit 6, 0 ON
320   LPRINT CHR$(32);    : GOSUB 1000: REM Bit 5 ON
330   LPRINT CHR$(130);   : GOSUB 1000: REM Bit 7, 1 ON
340   LPRINT CHR$(4);     : GOSUB 1000: REM Bit 2 ON
350   GOTO 300

400   REM Rotate Left
410   LPRINT CHR$(66);    : GOSUB 1000: REM Bit 6, 1 ON
420   LPRINT CHR$(32);    : GOSUB 1000: REM Bit 5 ON
430   LPRINT CHR$(129);   : GOSUB 1000: REM Bit 7, 0 ON
440   LPRINT CHR$(4);     : GOSUB 1000: REM Bit 2 ON
450   GOTO 400

500   REM Rotate Right
510   LPRINT CHR$(66);    : GOSUB 1000: REM Bit 6, 1 ON
520   LPRINT CHR$(4);     : GOSUB 1000: REM Bit 2 ON
530   LPRINT CHR$(129);   : GOSUB 1000: REM Bit 7, 0 ON
540   LPRINT CHR$(32);    : GOSUB 1000: REM Bit 5 ON
550   GOTO 500

1000  REM Check Key Press and Do Delay Loop
1010  A$ = INKEY$
1020  IF A$ = " " THEN PRINT "Stop": LPRINT CHR$(0); : GOTO 100
1030  IF A$ = CHR$(0) + "H" THEN PRINT "Forward": LPRINT CHR$(0); : GOTO 200
1050  IF A$ = CHR$(0) + "P" THEN PRINT "Reverse": LPRINT CHR$(0); : GOTO 300
1060  IF A$ = CHR$(0) + "K" THEN PRINT "Left": LPRINT CHR$(0); : GOTO 400
1070  IF A$ = CHR$(0) + "M" THEN PRINT "Right" : LPRINT CHR$(0); : GOTO 500
1080  IF A$ = "Q" OR A$ = "q" THEN LPRINT CHR$(0); : END

1100  FOR I = 1 TO DELAY
1110  NEXT I
1120  RETURN

1900  END

RUN
```

Software listings of this program and more are available *free* on-line at the Mondo-tronics web site: **http://www.Mondo.com/mwpb/**

See the references section starting on page J-1 for more information.

Figure 3.85   Listings for Test Program Four
This program permits the operator to control Boris with simple keyboard commands. Pressing the Up arrow on the numeric keypad (#8) causes Boris to walk. The Down arrow makes it walk in reverse, and the Left and Right arrows cause it to rotate. Options include adding gripper hardware to Bits 3 and 4, and expanding these instructions to make a system that can walk around, pick up objects, and perform other telerobotic tasks.

Figure 3.86 Boris
Just the first step.

Variations

The possible variations for Boris are limitless:

• Add foot pads for different terrains; rocky, powdery or carpeted surfaces need larger diameter pads, smooth surfaces need smaller ones; use non-slip rubber for very smooth surfaces.

• Create a lightweight shell and leg covers with an exotic design.

• Add a manipulator and control it via Bits 3 and 4 to pick up ping-pong balls.

• Add sensors on the foot pads and legs to make a true sensory/actuator robot system that can avoid objects.

• Add tiny batteries and an on-board controller for an autonomous roving robot not limited by the harness length.

• Make a waterproof Boris that can swim or walk along underwater. (Hint: faster cooling rates mean faster actions!)

• Add a tiny camera and broadcast signals back from remote locations.

• Add two cameras and send back 3-D images.

• Make the cameras waterproof, add lights and send it down the deep water wells beneath Texas to explore the sunless ecology recently found there.[44] Send back pictures and videos of the mysterious inhabitants, and investigate their source of energy.

• Build a team of remote controlled, solar-powered Boris robots and send them to the Moon with a low-cost *Pegasus* launcher via an efficient *fuzzy boundary* transfer orbit.[45] Sell time to adventurers on Earth who can then explore the Moon from their living rooms!

• Send another team of robots with more intelligence outward to explore the deserts, canyons and ice caps of Mars.

• Then prepare for the dozens of amazing worlds circling the giant planets. The stars await!

Like all great journeys, this too, begins with but a single step. Foot pads ready...

Go!

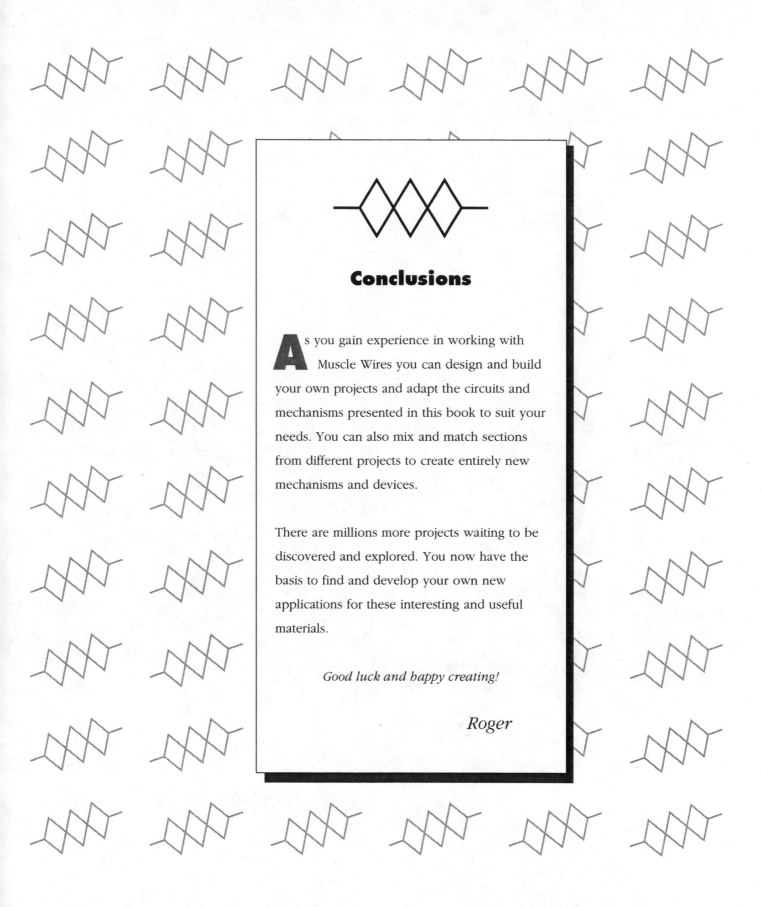

Conclusions

As you gain experience in working with Muscle Wires you can design and build your own projects and adapt the circuits and mechanisms presented in this book to suit your needs. You can also mix and match sections from different projects to create entirely new mechanisms and devices.

There are millions more projects waiting to be discovered and explored. You now have the basis to find and develop your own new applications for these interesting and useful materials.

Good luck and happy creating!

Roger

Pattern Sheets

Project 2 — Basic Lever
Page 3-6

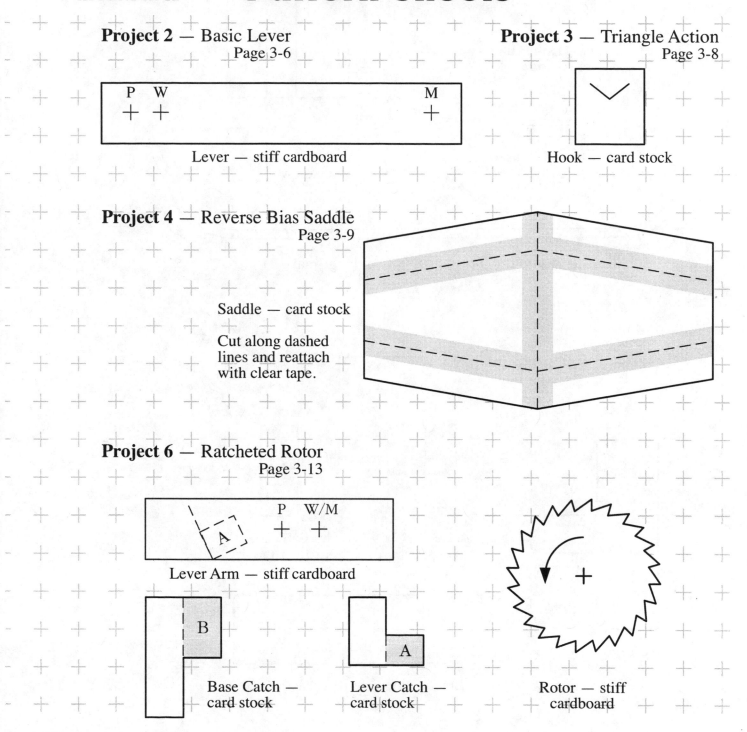

P W   M
+ +   +

Lever — stiff cardboard

Project 3 — Triangle Action
Page 3-8

Hook — card stock

Project 4 — Reverse Bias Saddle
Page 3-9

Saddle — card stock

Cut along dashed
lines and reattach
with clear tape.

Project 6 — Ratcheted Rotor
Page 3-13

P   W/M
+   +

A

Lever Arm — stiff cardboard

B

Base Catch —
card stock

A

Lever Catch —
card stock

Rotor — stiff
cardboard

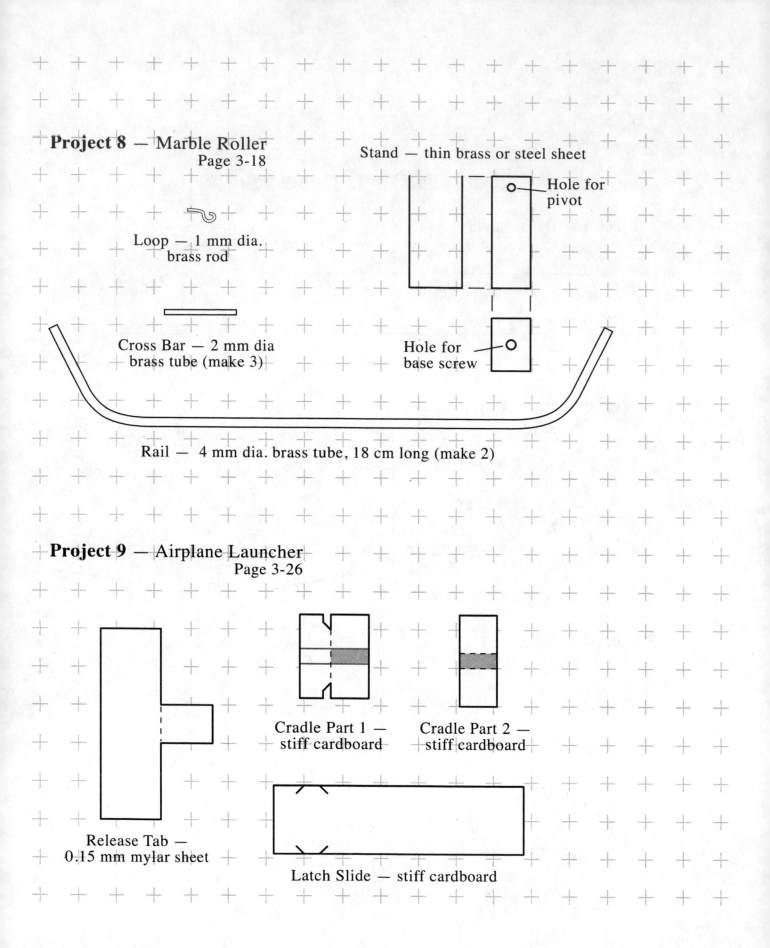

Project 8 — Marble Roller
Page 3-18

Stand — thin brass or steel sheet

Hole for pivot

Loop — 1 mm dia. brass rod

Cross Bar — 2 mm dia brass tube (make 3)

Hole for base screw

Rail — 4 mm dia. brass tube, 18 cm long (make 2)

Project 9 — Airplane Launcher
Page 3-26

Cradle Part 1 — stiff cardboard

Cradle Part 2 — stiff cardboard

Release Tab — 0.15 mm mylar sheet

Latch Slide — stiff cardboard

Project 12 — Life-like Butterfly
Page 3-29

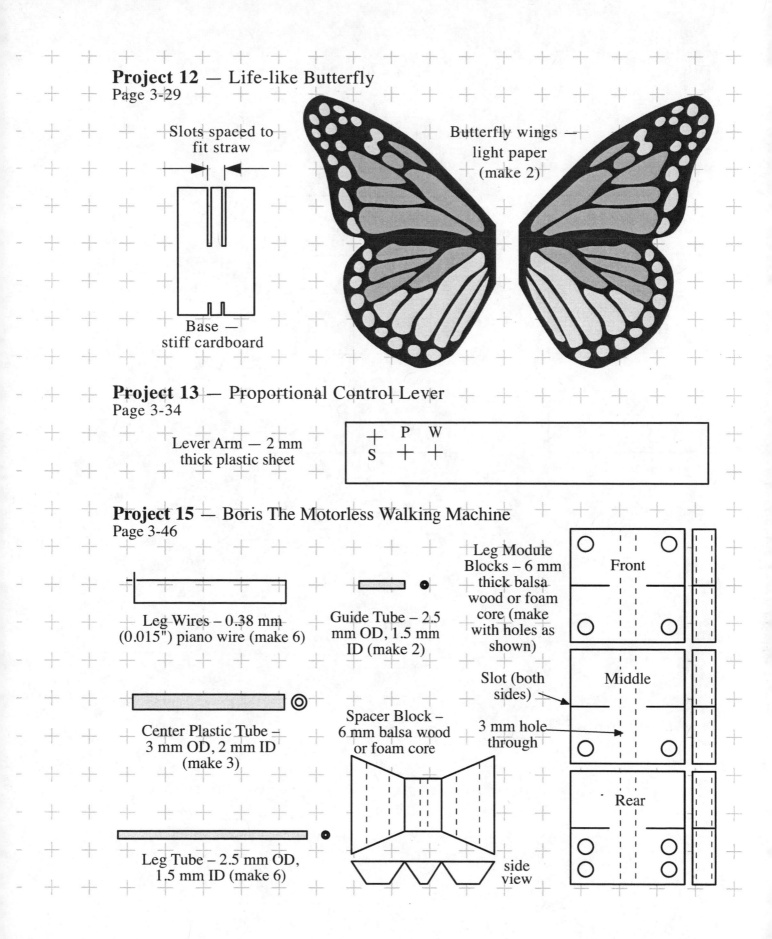

Slots spaced to fit straw

Base — stiff cardboard

Butterfly wings — light paper (make 2)

Project 13 — Proportional Control Lever
Page 3-34

Lever Arm — 2 mm thick plastic sheet

+ P W
S + +

Project 15 — Boris The Motorless Walking Machine
Page 3-46

Leg Wires – 0.38 mm (0.015") piano wire (make 6)

Guide Tube – 2.5 mm OD, 1.5 mm ID (make 2)

Leg Module Blocks – 6 mm thick balsa wood or foam core (make with holes as shown)

Front

Center Plastic Tube – 3 mm OD, 2 mm ID (make 3)

Spacer Block – 6 mm balsa wood or foam core

Slot (both sides)

Middle

3 mm hole through

Leg Tube – 2.5 mm OD, 1.5 mm ID (make 6)

side view

Rear

Leg Panel – 1 mm thick
plastic sheet (make 6)

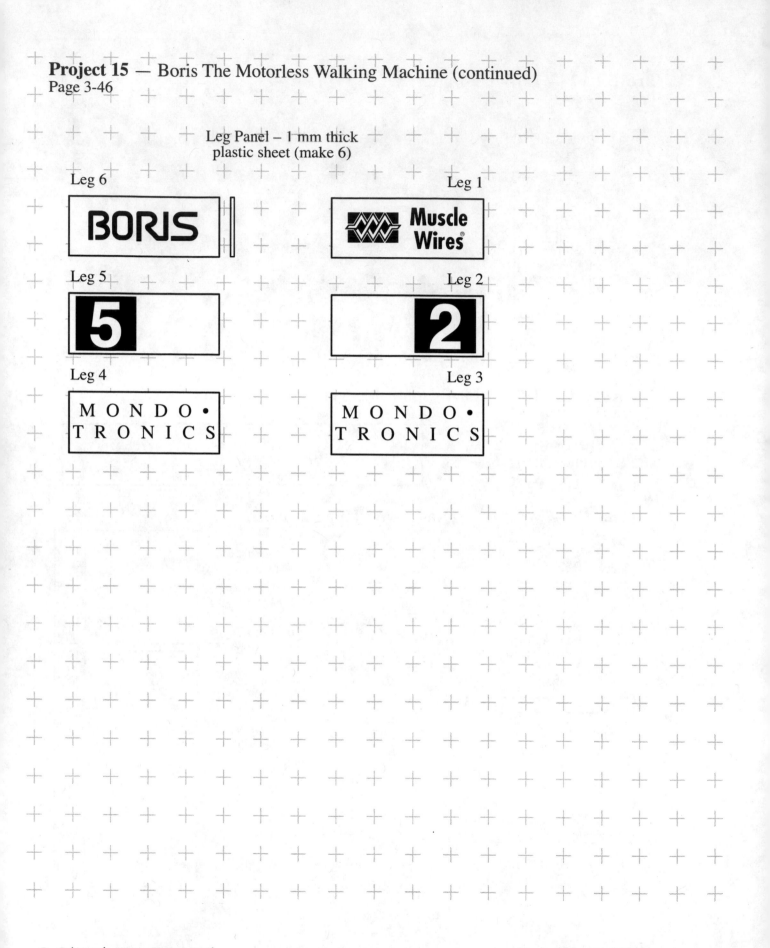

Leg 6

Leg 1

Leg 5

Leg 2

Leg 4

Leg 3

APPENDIX B

Metric System & Conversions

This book uses measurements in the metric system, first developed and implemented in France in 1795. The United States Congress approved the metric system for use in the U.S. in 1866.

The metric system consists of seven standard units of measure:

meter	length
kilogram	mass
second	time
ampere	electric current
Kelvin	temp. above absolute zero
mole	amount of substance
candela	luminous intensity

Other useful measures come from the basic seven, such as the *liter* (one thousand cubic centimeters), and the *newton* (the force needed to accelerate one kilogram one meter per second squared).

Note that MASS is the *amount* of substance, and WEIGHT is the *force* exerted by a mass when pulled by a gravity field.

	Measure	Abbreviation	Amount
LENGTH	micrometer (or micron)	μm	0.000,001
	millimeter	mm	0.001
	centimeter	cm	0.01
	decimeter	dm	0.1
	meter	m	1
	dekameter	dam	10
	hectometer	hm	100
	kilometer	km	1,000
MASS	milligram	mg	0.001
	gram	g	1
	kilogram	kg	1,000
	metric ton	t	1,000,000

WEIGHT Multiply mass in kilograms by 9.8 m/s² (the acceleration of gravity at the Earth's surface) to obtain weight in newtons.

TEMPERATURE When you know temperature in Celsius (°C):
Add 273.16 to get Kelvin.

When you know temperature in Kelvin (K):
Subtract 273.16 to get Celsius.

Figure B.1 Metric Units of Length, Mass, Weight, and Kelvin Temperature Conversion

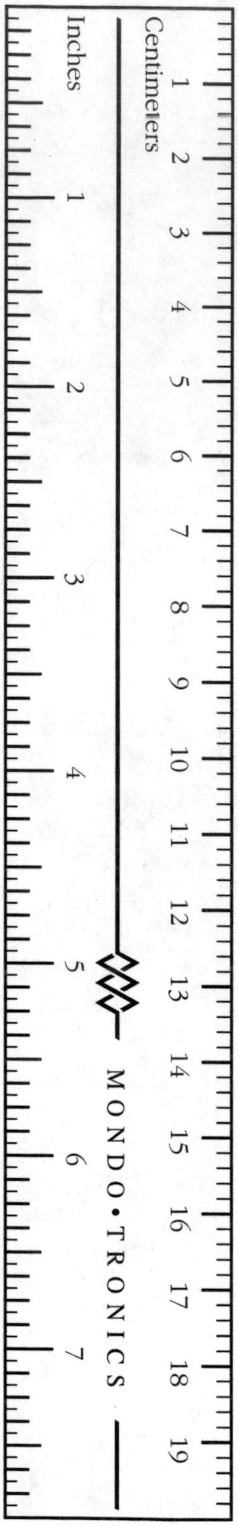

Metric – U.S. / U.S. – Metric Conversions

	If you know	Multiply by	To get
LENGTH	micrometer	0.04	mil (thousandths of an inch)
	millimeter	0.04	inches
	centimeters	0.39	inches
	meters	3.28	feet
	meters	1.09	yards
	kilometers	0.62	miles
	mil	25.40	micrometer
	inches	25.40	millimeters
	inches	2.54	centimeters
	feet	30.48	centimeters
	yards	0.91	meters
	miles	1.61	kilometers
AREA	square centimeters	0.16	square inches
	square meters	10.8	square feet
	square meters	1.20	square yards
	square kilometers	0.39	square miles
	square inches	6.45	square centimeters
	square feet	0.09	square meters
	square yards	0.84	square meters
	square miles	2.60	square kilometers
MASS	grams	0.035	ounces
	kilograms	2.21	pound mass
	metric tons (1000 kg)	1.10	short tons
	ounces	28.35	grams
	pound mass	0.45	kilograms
	short tons (2000 lbs)	0.91	metric tons
FORCE & WEIGHT	newton	0.2248	pound force
	pound force	4.448	newton
PRESSURE	megapascal	145	pounds per square inch
	pounds per square inch	0.006895	megapascal
VOLUME	milliliters	0.03	fluid ounces
	liters	0.26	gallons
	fluid ounces	29.57	milliliters
	gallons	3.79	liters

TEMPERATURE

When you know temperature in Celsius (°C):
Multiply by 9, divide by 5, and add 32 to get Fahrenheit.

When you know temperature in Fahrenheit (°F):
Subtract 32, multiply by 5, and divide by 9 to get Celsius.

Fig B.2   Centimeters & Inches   **Figure B.3   Converting Metric and U.S. Units**

Soldering Electronics

If you have never assembled electronics you should read about the basics before starting. The following outline gives the basic steps for preparing, soldering and inspecting many kinds of electronic parts.

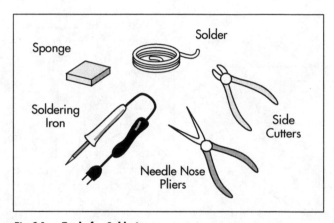

Fig C.1   Tools for Soldering

With a few tools and a little patience you should have no trouble assembling, testing and running the projects described in this book.

Tools

You will need the items shown in Figure C.1: a soldering iron for electronics, a small sponge, electronic solder, needle nose pliers, and side cutters. Also helpful are a stand for the soldering iron, and a desoldering bulb or soldering wick for removing solder.

Starting

Plug in the soldering iron and allow a minute or two for it to heat. Moisten the sponge with a small amount of water.

When hot, "tin" the soldering iron's tip with a small amount of solder. It should be shiny and coated with solder. If it is dry or refuses to hold the solder, or if the tip is old or corroded, replace the tip.

Wipe the tip across the sponge from time to time to keep it clean. A clean, well-tinned tip does the best job.

Steps:

Bend the component leads to fit the holes on the circuit board. (See Figure C.2-A)

Insert the part into the circuit board (C.2-B), and bend the leads enough to

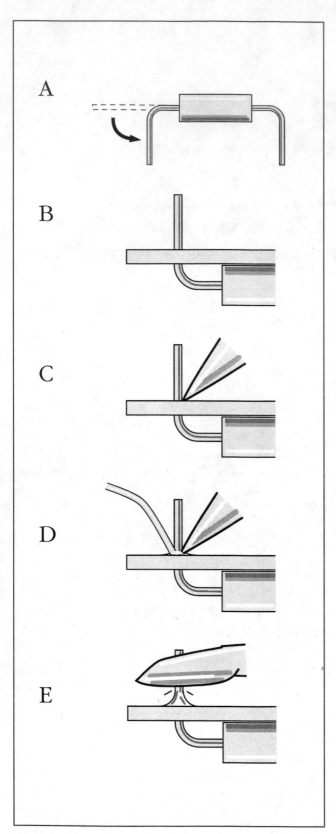

Fig C.2   Soldering Steps
Bend leads (A), insert into board (B), heat (C), apply solder (D), let cool and trim excess lead (E).

hold the part against the board, but don't over bend.

Wipe the tip clean on the moist sponge and "tin" it with a small amount of solder.

Heat the joint by placing the tinned tip against the component lead and the circuit board pad (Fig. C.2-C). After a moment of heating, touch the solder to the lead, pad and iron (Fig. C.2-D). When the solder flows, remove it, and hold the tip in place for 1 second.

Remove the soldering iron and let the joint cool without letting the part or board move.

Trim excess component lead with the side cutter (Fig. C.2-E). Parts with naturally short leads do not need to be trimmed. Inspect the joint. A good solder joint blends the lead and pad smoothly together, and has a smooth, bright finish.

If the joint bulges or bridges to other pads, remelt it, and remove the excess solder with the soldering iron. If the joint looks fuzzy or dull it is a "cold" solder joint. Remelt it, and let it cool (without moving) to a smooth, bright finish.

For more information on soldering and basic electronics, refer to the sources listed in the references section starting on page J-1.

Calculating Triangle Actuators

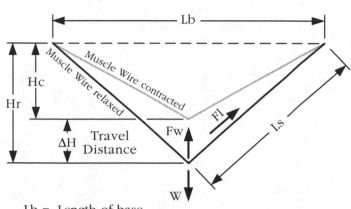

Lb = Length of base

Ls = Length of side (half the length of the Muscle Wire. Total Wire Length = 2 x Ls)

%L = Percent change in wire length (usually 3 to 5%)

Hr = Height of triangle relaxed (Muscle Wire cooled)

$$= \sqrt{Ls^2 - (0.25 \times Lb^2)}$$

Hc = Height of triangle contracted (Muscle Wire heated)

$$= \sqrt{(Ls \times (\%L / 100))^2 - (0.25 \times Lb^2)}$$

ΔH = Change in height (the usable motion)

$$= Hr - Hc$$

Fl = Force of wire in a linear or straight-line contraction (the wire's Recommended Recovery Force). See page 2-5.

%F = Percentage of Fl exerted to lift the weight W (the rest is exerted horizontally against the anchor points)

$$= Sin (Arctan ((2 \times Hr) / Lb)))$$

Fw = Force of wire to lift the weight W

$$= 2 \times \%F \times Fl$$

The geometry of the triangle actuator provides an easy way to exchange force for distance when using Muscle Wires. The triangle easily converts the large force and small motion of a Muscle Wire into a smaller force that moves a larger distance.

Varying the height of the triangle (Hr in the figure to the left) results in travel distances from the maximum contraction of the Muscle Wire, down to zero. Likewise, the force Fw varies from zero up to twice the wire's linear contraction force (there are two wires pulling in parallel at the deepest "U" shaped triangle).

Use these equations to calculate the changes in height and force for a wire of given strength and size.

Entering the equations into a spreadsheet program provides a flexible tool for developing and refining triangle actuators. Projects 2 and 7 use the triangle geometry, and can serve as the starting point for many additional mechanisms.

Table of Flexinol Muscle Wire Properties

Properties	Flexinol Name	025	037	050	075	100	125	150	200	250	300	375
Physical	Wire Diameter (µm)	25	37	50	75	100	125	150	200	250	300	375
	Minimum Ben Radius (mm)	1.3	1.85	2.5	3.75	5.0	6.25	7.5	10.0	12.50	15.0	18.75
	Cross-sectional Area (µm²)	490	1,075	1,960	4,420	7,850	12,270	17,700	31,420	49,100	70,700	110,450
Electrical	Linear Resistance (Ω/m)	1,770	860	510	200	150	70	50	31	20	13	8
	Recommended Current† (mA)	20	30	50	100	180	250	400	610	1,000	1,750	2,750
	Recommended Power† (W/m)	0.71	0.78	1.28	2.0	4.86	4.4	8.00	12.0	20.0	39.8	60.5
Strength* Max. Recovery Weight @ 600 MPa (g)		29	65	117	250	469	736	1,056	1,860	2,933	4,240	6,630
	Rec. Recovery Weight @ 190 MPa (g)	7	20	35	80	150	230	330	590	930	1,250	2,000
	Rec. Deformation Weight @ 35 MPa (g)	2	4	8	815	28	43	62	110	172	245	393
Speed	Typical Contraction Speed†† (sec)	1.0	1.0	1.0	1.0	1.0	1.0	1.0	1.0	1.0	1.0	1.0
	LT Relaxation Speed†† (sec)	0.16	0.25	0.3	0.5	0.8	1.6	2.0	3.5	5.5	8.0	13.0
	LT Alloy Thermal Cycle Rate (cyc/min)	52	48	46	40	33	23	20	13	9	7	4
	HT Relaxation Speed†† (sec)	n.a.	0.09	0.1	0.2	0.4	0.9	1.2	2.2	3.5	6	10
	HT Alloy Thermal Cycle Rate (cyc/min)	n.a.	55	55	50	43	32	27	19	13	9	5

		LT Alloy	HT Alloy
Thermal	Activation Start Temp. (°C)	68	88
	Activation Finish Temp. (°C)	78	98
	Relaxation Start Temp. (°C)	52	72
	Relaxation Finish Temp. (°C)	42	62
	Annealing Temp. (°C)	300	300
	Melting Temp. (°C)	1,300	1,300
	Specific Heat (cal/g°C)	0.077	0.077
	Heat Capacity (Joule/g°C)	0.32	0.32
	Latent Heat (Joule/g)	24.2	24.2

Material			
	Density (g/cc)	6.45	
	Maximum Recovery Force (MPa)	600	(~43 ton / in²)
	Recommended Deformation Force (MPa)	35	(~2.5 ton / in²)
	Breaking Strength (MPa)	1,000	(~71 ton / in²)
	Poisson's Ratio	0.33	
	Work Output (Joule/g)	1	
	Energy Conversion Efficiency (%)	5	
	Maximum Deformation Ratio (%)	8	
	Recommended Deformation Ratio (%)	3-5	

Phase Related		Martensite	Austenite
	Phase		
	Resistivity (µΩcm)	76	82
	Young's Modulus (GPa)	28	75
	Magnetic Susceptibility (µemu/g)	2.5	3.8
	Thermal Conductivity (W/cm°C)	0.08	0.18

† In still air, at 20°C.

* To obtain force in Newtons,
multiply mass in grams by 0.0098.

†† Depends greatly on local heating
and cooling conditions. See text.

Also see Part Two for more about
the properties of Muscle Wires.

Roger G. Gilbertson

Electronic Symbols

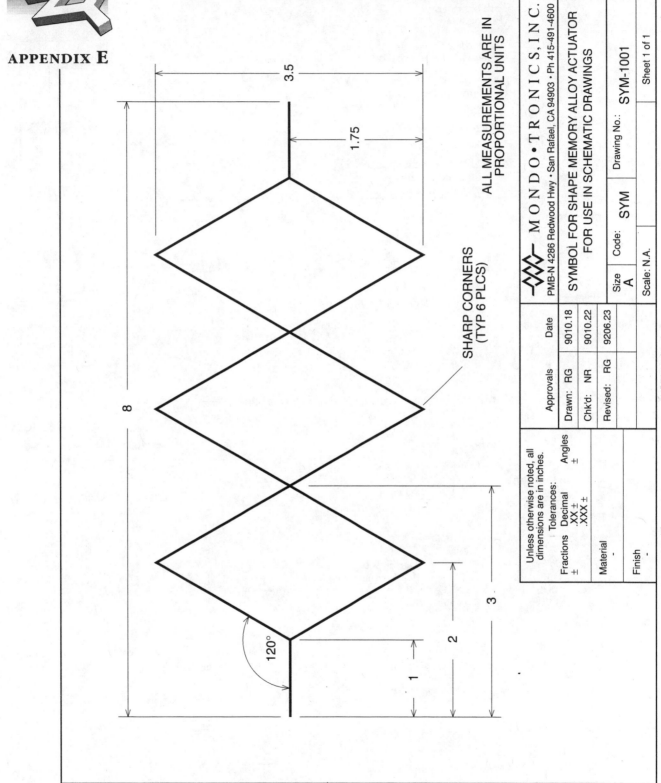

3.5

1.75

8

SHARP CORNERS
(TYP 6 PLCS)

120°

1

2

3

ALL MEASUREMENTS ARE IN
PROPORTIONAL UNITS

MONDO•TRONICS, INC.
PMB-N 4286 Redwood Hwy • San Rafael, CA 94903 • Ph 415-491-4600

SYMBOL FOR SHAPE MEMORY ALLOY ACTUATOR
FOR USE IN SCHEMATIC DRAWINGS

	Approvals	Date
Drawn:	RG	9010.18
Chk'd:	NR	9010.22
Revised:	RG	9206.23

Size	Code:	Drawing No.:
A	SYM	SYM-1001

Scale: N.A. | | Sheet 1 of 1

Unless otherwise noted, all
dimensions are in inches.
Tolerances:

Fractions	Decimal	Angles
±	.XX ±	±
	.XXX ±	

Material
-

Finish
-

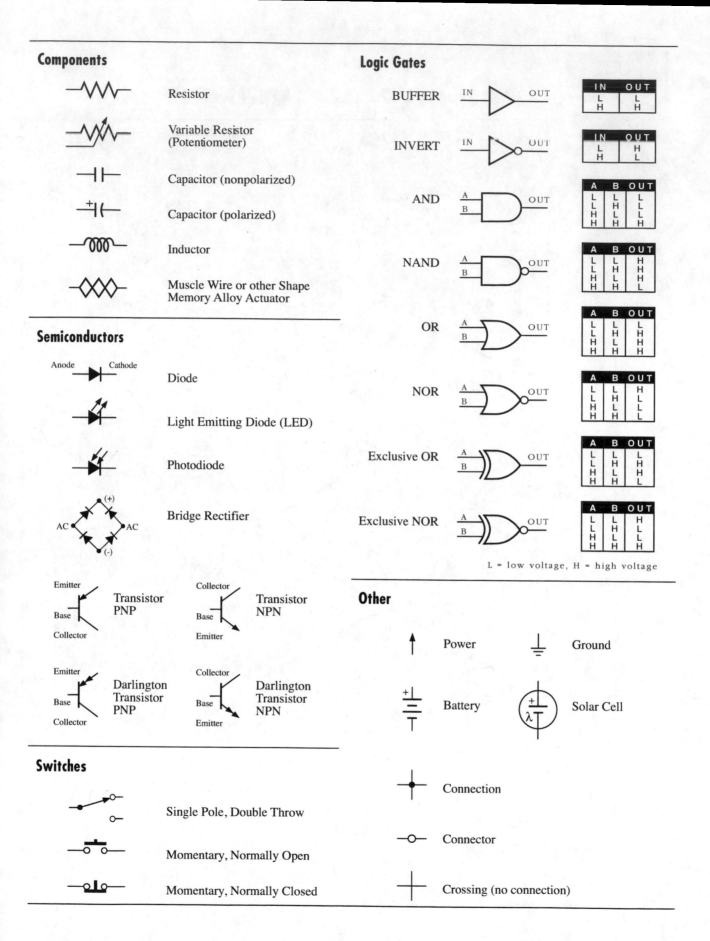

Components

- Resistor
- Variable Resistor (Potentiometer)
- Capacitor (nonpolarized)
- Capacitor (polarized)
- Inductor
- Muscle Wire or other Shape Memory Alloy Actuator

Semiconductors

- Diode — Anode / Cathode
- Light Emitting Diode (LED)
- Photodiode
- Bridge Rectifier — (+), AC, AC, (-)
- Transistor PNP — Emitter, Base, Collector
- Transistor NPN — Collector, Base, Emitter
- Darlington Transistor PNP — Emitter, Base, Collector
- Darlington Transistor NPN — Collector, Base, Emitter

Switches

- Single Pole, Double Throw
- Momentary, Normally Open
- Momentary, Normally Closed

Logic Gates

BUFFER — IN / OUT

IN	OUT
L	L
H	H

INVERT — IN / OUT

IN	OUT
L	H
H	L

AND — A, B / OUT

A	B	OUT
L	L	L
L	H	L
H	L	L
H	H	H

NAND — A, B / OUT

A	B	OUT
L	L	H
L	H	H
H	L	H
H	H	L

OR — A, B / OUT

A	B	OUT
L	L	L
L	H	H
H	L	H
H	H	H

NOR — A, B / OUT

A	B	OUT
L	L	H
L	H	L
H	L	L
H	H	L

Exclusive OR — A, B / OUT

A	B	OUT
L	L	L
L	H	H
H	L	H
H	H	L

Exclusive NOR — A, B / OUT

A	B	OUT
L	L	H
L	H	L
H	L	L
H	H	H

L = low voltage, H = high voltage

Other

- Power
- Ground
- Battery
- Solar Cell
- Connection
- Connector
- Crossing (no connection)

APPENDIX F

Footnotes

1. D. Stöckel, "Thermal Actuation with Shape Memory Alloys". Raychem Corp., p 3.

2. A. Ölander, "Ztsch. Krist.", 1932.

3. L.C. Chang and T.A. Read, "The Gold-Cadmium Beta Phase". Trans. AIME, Vol. 191, p 47, 1951.

4. "BioMetal Guidebook". Toki Corp.., Tokyo, Japan, 1986.

5. W.J. Buehler, J.V. Gilfrich and R.C. Wiley, Journal of Applied Physics, Vol 34, p 1475, 1963, and Buehler, W.J., et al., U.S. Patent 3,174,851 issued 1965.

6. K. Shimizu and T. Tadaki, "Shape Memory Alloys", H. Funakubo ed. Gordon and Breach Science Pub., 1987.

7. D.E. Hodgson, "Using Shape Memory Alloys". Shape Memory Applications, Inc., Cupertino, CA, 1988.

8. C.M. Jackson et al., "55-Nitinol - The Alloy with a Memory". NASA Pub. SP–5110, Washington, DC, 1972.

9. L.S. Castleman and S.M. Motzkin, "The Biocompatibility of Nitinol". In "Biocompatibility of Clinical Implant Materials, Vol. 1" edited by D.F. Williams, p 129, 1981.

10. M. Page and P.N. Sawyer, "Prosthetic Pump". U.S. Patent 3,827,426, issued 1974.

11. "Catching Lethal Blood Clots", FOCUS. Harvard University News Office, June 7, 1990.

12. J. Zauda, "The Engine That Runs on Sunshine". Popular Science, April 1974.

13. A.D. Johnson, private conversation, 12/90.

14. J.L. McNichols et al., "Final Report - Prototype Nitinol Heat Engine", MDC G9290. McDonnell Douglas Company, Huntington Beach, CA, 1980.

15. Raychem Corporation, "Tinel Shape-Memory Alloys" product brochure.

16. A. Velocci, "New Connector Opens the Door to Smaller, More Cost-Effective Electronic Packaging". Aviation Week, Sep 3, 1990.

17. Innovative Technology International, Inc., "Nitinol" product brochure.

18. T.W. Duerig and K.N. Melton, "Designing With The Shape Memory Effect". Proceedings of Materials Research Society International Symposium on Shape Memory Materials. K. Otsuka and K. Shimizu eds., p 581, 1989. Has references to over 180 reports from around the world.

19. Furukawa Electric Co., Ltd., "Furukawa NT Alloy" product brochure.

20. "Metallic Recall". Popular Science, p 72, Dec 1988.

21. L.H. McCarty, "Special Alloy Is Key To Braille Computer Display". Design News, p 158, Feb 12, 1990.

22. C. Youyi et al., "Shape Memory Alloy '86 - Proceedings of the International Symposium on Shape Memory Alloys". China Academic Publishers, Beijing, China, 1986.

23. "Engineering Aspects Of Shape Memory Alloys". Edited by T.W. Duerig. Published by Butterworth–Heinemann Ltd., England, 1990.

24. F. Seamon, Seatek. Private conversation, 5/19/92.

25. Philip E. Myers. Private letter, 3/20/92.

26. K. Kuribayashi, "Millimeter-sized Joint Actuator Using a Shape Memory Alloy". Sensors and Actuators 20, p 57, 1989.

27. Phillip Shaw. Private letter, 1/5/92.

28. Nakano, Y. et al., "Hitachi's Robot Hand". Robotics Age, p 18, July 1984.

29. Tini Alloy Company, "TiNi Pneumatic Valves" product brochure.

30. R. Jebens, W. Trimmer, J. Walker, "Microacutators for Aligning Optical Fibers". Sensors and Actuators 20, p 65, 1989.

31. L.H. McCarty, "Shape Memory Alloy Actuates Separation Device". Design News, p 78, Jan 21, 1991.

32. H. Rheingold, "Travels in Virtual Reality". Whole Earth Review No. 67, p 80, Summer 1990.

33. J.D. Busch et al., "Shape-memory Properties in Ni-Ti Sputter-deposited Films", J. Appl. Phys. 68 (12), p 6224, Dec. 15, 1990.

34. R.C.L. Sachdeva and S. Miyazaki, "Superelastic Ni-Ti Alloys in Orthodontics". Ibid., p 452.

35. J.P O'Leary, J.E. Nicholson, R.F. Gatturna, "The Use of Ni-Ti in the Homer Mammalok". Ibid., p 477.

36. Marchon Eyewear, Inc. U.S., Patent Nos. 4,772,112 and 4,896,955.

37. M. Igharo and J.V. Wood, "Effect of Rapid Solidification Processing on Shape Memory Characteristics of Equiatomic TiNi". The Open University, Walton Hall, Milton Keynes, MK7 6AA, United Kingdom.

38. Eric E. Sabelman, "Detecting and preventing falls in the elderly". ON CENTER Technology Transfer News, Rehabilitation R&D Center, Veterans Administration Medical Center, Palo Alto, CA. USA. June 1992.

39. R.A. Brooks, "New Approaches to Robotics". Science, Vol. 253, p 1127, Sep 13, 1991.

40. A.M. Flynn, R.A. Brooks, W.M. Wells III, D.S. Barrett, "Intelligence for Miniature Robots". Sensors and Actuators 20, p 187, 1989.

41. E.C. Okress, "The Franklin Institute has high hopes for its big balloon". IEEE Spectrum, Dec 1978.

42. Buckminster Fuller Institute, 111 N. Main St., Sebastopol, CA 95472 USA. 707-824-2242 or 800-967-6277, www.bfi.org.

43. R.A. Brooks, A.M. Flynn, "Fast, Cheap and Out of Control". Journal of the British Interplanetary Society, Vol. 42, p 478, 1989.

44. E. Pennisi, "Saving Hades' Creatures". Science News, Vol 143, p 172, Mar 13, 1993.

45. E. Belbruno, "Through the Fuzzy Boundary: A New Route to the Moon", *Planetary Report*, Vol XII, No 3, May/June 1992, p 8, The Planetary Society, 65 North Catalina Ave., Pasadena, CA 91106 USA.

APPENDIX G

Index and List of Figures

List of Figures

Roger G. Gilbertson

APPENDIX H

Afterword

The Author

Roger Gilbertson's life changed at age four when he learned how to tear tape from the dispenser, thus gaining the ability to put things together. Since then, he has mastered many other techniques for assembling devices. And he still uses a lot of tape.

In college, Roger combined his wide ranging interests and produced a film and computer study of the walking patterns of legged animals.

This research inspired plans for robot mechanisms that adopted many of the structures of living creatures, but these designs proved difficult to build using electric motors.

Roger wrote in his research note book,

"needed... a material that contracts (or expands) when electrically stimulated – a kind of electric muscle fiber".

Just two years later, he found it.

While working for a Silicon Valley electronics company, Roger came across samples of a Japanese-made shape memory alloy wire. He knew immediately how to utilize it, and began building mechanisms and eventually working with the manufacturer.

In 1986, Roger and his friend Chris Paine founded the company Mondo-tronics, Inc. to facilitate shape memory alloy development and to distribute products, information, and enthusiasm for this rapidly developing technology.

Mondo-tronics

Mondo-tronics develops products for customers in North America, Europe and Japan, and has introduced thousands of engineers, students, and experimenters to the uses and benefits of shape memory alloy wires.

The Mondo-tronics team provides training, educational materials, and custom designs using the latest in shape memory technology. Customers include C.R. Bard Medical, Neiman Marcus, Show Biz Pizzatime Theaters, The

Nature Company, Toki, NASA/JPL, Lucasfilm's Industrial Light and Magic, Boeing, The Buckminster Fuller Institute, and students and teachers at schools of all levels.

Some of Mondo-tronics' awards include:

• Western Association of Visual Merchandisers "Most Innovative New Product" for "Kinetic Butterflies", a motorless display animation system. April 1988.

• Popular Science Magazine "Best of What's New 1988" for innovative use of new materials in the "Space Wings" hobby electronics kit. Nov 1988.

• Robotics Society of America Robot Races, Best Combined Score, 1st Place to "Satellite" microprocessor controlled line-following robot with Upstart Robots. Sep 1990.

• B.E.A.M. Robot Olympic Games, 1st Place "Innovation" Gold Medal award for Boris, a motorless miniature walking machine, with Upstart Robots. April 1993.

Future Developments

New and exciting opportunities await further development in a wide range of fields:

• *Medical – precision tools, filters, remote manipulators, prosthetic limbs, spine straighteners, bone growth devices.*

• *Industrial – miniaturized valves, relays, switches, circuit breakers, temperature control devices, mechanical actuators.*

• *Computers, electronics and communications – fiber optic connectors, fiber switches, miniature tools and manipulators, mini and micromini robotic devices.*

• *Toy and hobby – miniature mechanisms, animated dolls, action figure, animated books, cards, and posters, educational science kits, electronic and robotic projects.*

• *Earth and space exploration – high performance connectors, fittings, release mechanisms, miniature actuators, remotely operated manipulators, robotic devices for exploring underwater, the planets and outer space.*

• *Entertainment and virtual reality – motion picture special effects, tele-operated manipulators, tactile detectors, tactile displays, tactile fabric*

Please contact us regarding specific developments in these and other areas.

This Book

The first edition of this book grew out of requests for a comprehensive educational guide and project book demonstrating the many applications of shape memory alloy wires.

This latest edition has been completely revised and serves as a compendium for Mondo-tronics' years of research, experience and wisdom. It incorporates the comments and suggestions from researchers, manufacturers and other pivotal figures in the shape memory alloy field, as well as feedback from our valued customers.

Roger G. Gilbertson

APPENDIX J

References & Sources

Electronic Components

For basic electronic components by mail, contact these sources. They all have information packed catalogs and complete lines of parts, tools and accessories.

> Digi-Key Corporation
> 701 Brooks Avenue South
> Thief River Falls, MN 56701
> > Phone 800-344-4539 or 218-681-6674
> > Fax 218-681-3380
> > Web www.DigiKey.com

> Jameco Electronics
> 1355 Shoreway Road
> Belmont, CA 94002
> > Phone 800-831-4242 or 650-592-8097
> > Fax 650-592-2503
> > Web www.Jameco.com

> Mouser Electronics
> 958 North Main
> Mansfield, TX 76063
> > Phone 800-346-6873 or 817-483-4422
> > Fax 817-483-0931
> > Web www.Mouser.com

Basic Electronics Information

If you are just beginning to work with electronics, or if you need a good reference for basic electronic components and circuits, check out "Getting Started in Electronics" by Forrest M. Mims, III. Published by Radio Shack (Cat. No. 276-5003).

Visit your local library and newsstands for electronics and robotics publications where you will find lots of new projects and ideas. Some titles include: *Poptronics, Midnight Engineering, Nuts & Volts,* Steve Ciarcia's *Circuit Cellar INK* and *Robot Science & Technology.* Also watch for magazines on specialized hobbies like model railroads, and radio controlled modeling for additional useful projects and information.

Muscle Wires

Now that you have explored the basics of Muscle Wires, you most likely have dozens of projects in mind, and need a source for Muscle Wires.

Mondo-tronics has been distributing shape memory alloy products and kits since 1986. We feature Flexinol Muscle Wires, project kits, information and other related products, and performs research and product development for companies around the world in a variety of fields. Contact us or visit our web site for details.

> **Mondo-tronics, Inc.**
> 4460 Redwood Hwy., #16-307
> San Rafael, CA 94903
> > Phone: 415-491-4600
> > Fax: 415-962-4039
> > Email: mondotronics@email.com
> > Web: http://www.Mondotronics.com

Web Site

http://www.MuscleWires.com

Visit our web site to receive the latest notes and additions to this book, to download software listings for the projects, to find current listings for Muscle Wires suppliers around the world, and for information on other related products kits, books and information.

BONUS 1

Free-Running Pendulum

Introduction

In this device a length of Muscle Wire drives a pendulum that will continuously oscillate once it has started swinging. This project demonstrates how the small but smooth and strong motion of Muscle Wires can be put to work in familiar mechanical systems, and how such devices can be simpler than traditional mechanical solutions.

Construction:

Sand one face of the wooden block until it is smooth. Nail the three nails part way into the wood as shown, and then pull them out again.

Prepare a length of magnet wire that is 10 cm longer than the Muscle Wire and sand both ends to remove the insulation. Crimp the magnet wire and Muscle Wire together making sure they do not slip out. From the remaining piece of magnet wire, prepare three pieces by sanding the insulation off each end. Also sand the lower half of each nail.

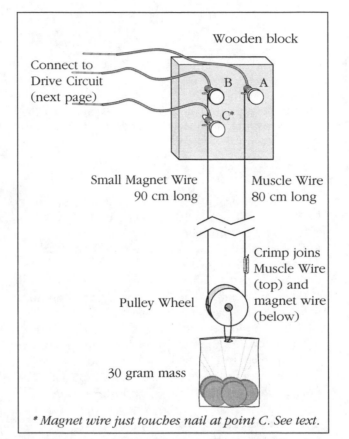

* Magnet wire just touches nail at point C. See text.

Figure 4.01   Pendulum Mechanism
The device demonstrates a way to convert the linear action of a Muscle Wire into a continuous swinging motion. The contact at point C senses the swing rate and reinforces the pendulum's natural frequency of oscillation.

In the hole labeled A place the free end of the Muscle Wire and one free end from one of the hook-up wires, wedging them securely with a nail. In the hole labeled B place the free end of the magnet wire and one free end from the second hook-up wire, securing them with the second nail. And into hole C place the third hook-up wire, securing it with the third nail.

Pendulum Parts List

1	each	Muscle Wire, 100 μm dia., 80-100 cm long
1	each	Crimp (N scale rail joiner or other)
3	each	Medium-sized nails
1	each	Small gauge magnet wire, insulated, 2 meters long
1	each	Wooden block, 8 x 8 x 1 cm thick, (3 x 3 x 0.5 in.)
1	each	Small pulley, 2 cm dia.
1	each	Small plastic bag
12	each	U.S. 1 cent coins (or other 30 gram mass)
		Sandpaper
		Thread

__Mark Valentine__ of Keesler AFB, MS, designed and built this clever and educational device that uses a Muscle Wire to swing a hanging mass at its natural frequency.

Mark received a Mondo-tronics merchandise certificate for sharing his design.

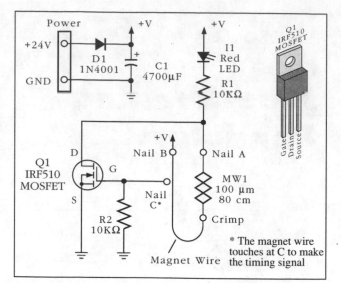

Figure 4.02   Drive Circuit
Connect the parts as shown, paying attention to how the thin magnet wire and Muscle Wire attach. Use a 24 volt power supply from a model train set, or similar.

Hang the pulley at the bottom of the Muscle Wire/magnet wire loop, and suspend the bag of 12 pennies through the center hole of the pulley. Letting the weight hang, sand the shiny insulation off the magnet wire where it touches the nail in the hole labeled C. This forms the contact for the timing signal.

Constructing the Driver Circuit:

This circuit is a snap. Locate components on the perf board and solder them together according to the schematic.

Plug in the power supply. Pull the bag of weights of the pendulum to one side and release it. The pendulum should swing continuously. The LED on the driver circuit should flash synchronously with the pendulum.

How it Works:

The main property of interest in a pendulum is that the time it takes to swing back and forth (its oscillation period) is largely independent of the size of the swing. That is how pendulums found their way into old mechanical clocks.

In theory, a perfect pendulum should swing forever. In reality, however, friction and air resistance combine to gradually slow it down. Winding a clock stores energy that the clock imparts to the pendulum at just the right instant during each swing.

In this device the Muscle Wire performs that function, adding a small amount of energy to each swing. By the laws governing a pendulum's swing and the conservation of angular momentum, the pendulum's motion remains very precise.

The length of the pendulum is such that the time required for the pendulum to travel from the lowest point in its swing to the highest equals the relaxation time and the construction time of the Muscle Wire.

This allows for a greater transfer of energy into the pendulum's swinging motions. The transistor switches the current through the Muscle Wire instead of using an electrical contact which would suffer from arcing due to the fairly high current.

Variations:

• Create displays and moving posters.

• Make a decorative pendulum for use in a Grandfather Clock (use a time limited circuit to make sure the Muscle Wire is never constantly energized).

• Make an electro-mechanical clock in which the pendulum supplies clock pulses to a counting circuit.